TREASURES
FROM
JAPAN

SCULPTURE
AND
DECORATIVE ARTS

A Special Loan Exhibition

FEBRUARY 1957

HONOLULU ACADEMY OF ARTS

The exhibition is held jointly by

Tokyo National Museum

and

Honolulu Academy of Arts

FOREWORD

Just two years ago, in February 1955, the Tokyo National Museum and the Honolulu Academy of Arts first joined forces to present a significant exhibition of great Japanese paintings from the collection of the Tokyo National Museum. That exhibition was undoubtedly the most successful showing of its kind in the Academy's history.

Now once again our two museums are engaged in a similar joint effort as documented by this catalogue. Much wider in scope, the current exhibition brings to Honolulu some two hundred masterpieces of sculpture, metalwork, ceramics, lacquer, masks, ivory carving, swords and sword furnishings, and archaeological artifacts. We are confident that this exhibition will enjoy an even greater popularity.

From the museum's point of view, one of the most heartening aspects of the 1955 exhibition was the fact that so many of the thousands of people who came to see it returned again and again to savor its spiritual and material richness. The greater variety of works of art shown in this exhibition makes repetitive visits almost a necessity. From ancient Haniwa tomb figures to comparatively modern kimono fabrics, the exhibition offers a dazzling survey of the exquisite sense of taste and the masterful technical proficiency characteristic of Japanese classical workmanship.

The Honolulu Academy of Arts is grateful and proud to have this opportunity to present this jointly sponsored exhibition to the residents of the Hawaiian Islands and to our visitors from all parts of the world. We are also extremely happy to have this second opportunity to work in intimate association with the Tokyo National Museum, and we are deeply indebted to Mr. Nagatake Asano, its director, and to his staff, whose interest, cooperation, and intensive labors have made the exhibition possible. Once again as in 1955, the preparation of this catalogue, the choice of the works of art shown, and the manifold responsibility of packing and shipping have been cheerfully assumed by these devoted scholars and administrators. The inevitable justification of their efforts must be the more profound appreciation and understanding of Japanese culture which these two exhibitions produce in the Western World.

Robert P. Griffing, Jr.
Director, Honolulu Academy of Arts

序　　文

　ちょうど2年前の1955年2月，東京国立博物館とホノルル美術館のはじめての共同主催として，東京国立博物館出品のすぐれた日本絵画を展観する有益な展覧会がひらかれた。この展覧会は当美術館の歴史においてこの種のものとして最大の成功をおさめたものであった。

　今ここに両館はふたたび力をあわせて同様のもよおしを開くにいたったことはこの図録に見られる通りである。この展覧会は前回よりはるかに広範囲にわたり，彫刻，金工，陶磁，漆工，仮面，牙彫り，刀装ならびに小道具，考古遺物など，約200点におよぶ優品をホノルルへもたらしたものである。この展覧会が前回にもまして多大の反響をよぶことは信じて疑わない。

　1955年度の展覧会の際，数万の観覧者のうちの非常に多くの人々が，その精神的，物質的豊かさを味わうために幾度もくり返し見に来たことは，美術館の立場として最も心強いことの一つであった。この度は出品の種類も多いことであるから，何回も見ていただくことはほとんど必要といえよう。古代墳墓をかざった埴輪から比較的近代のきものにいたるまで，日本工芸技術の特徴とする優秀な趣味感覚と至妙の技法的多彩さとは，さん然として本展覧会に綜合されていると言ってよい。

　ホノルル美術館は，この共同主催展をハワイ諸島の住民ならびに世界各国からおとずれる旅行者に贈る機会をもち得たことに対し，喜びと誇りをもつものである。われわれはここにふたたび東京国立博物館と親しく協力する機会を得たことを大いなる喜びとし，同館長および職員諸氏の熱意と協同と非常な努力によって本展覧会が開催のはこびにいたったことを深く感謝する。1955年度と同じく，このたびもまた本図録の編集，出品の選択，梱包出荷に関する諸般の仕事など，すべて同館の学者，責任者諸賢が進んで労をとって下さったものである。両度の展覧会により日本文化の鑑賞と理解が世界に深まることこそ，これらの人々のお骨折りに対する当然の報酬であろう。

ホノルル・アカデミー・オブ・アーツ

館長　　ロバート・P・グリフィング

PREFACE

In 1955 we had the first showing of Treasures from Japan at the Honolulu Academy of Arts. The project had long been the mutual desire of our two institutions, and its realization and success, almost beyond our expectation, remain as a happy recollection. That exhibition has caused us to feel as if Honolulu has become nearer than ever to Japan; people in Honolulu, on their part, must feel that Japan is now closer to them. The second showing was originally scheduled to be held in 1956. It was a matter of regret that it had to be postponed due to circumstances beyond our mutual control.

The postponement of a full year now only serves to enhance our joy in this second exhibition. As the first showing displayed paintings alone, this second and final one is dedicated to sculpture and decorative arts from ancient times to the "early modern" period. Japanese sculpture, as was the case with other aspects of Japanese arts, was deeply and frequently influenced by Chinese culture, but it has also much of the native Japanese character. Works of decorative art represent Japanese culture even more thoroughly. It appears that the Japanese flavor in matters of art and culture is attracting attention in America and Europe more than ever before, but in organizing the present exhibition we have not tried to ingratiate ourselves with this Western interest. Consisting of specimens selected on a wider basis, the collection contains some which may not appear purely Japanese. We should like to emphasize, however, that these, too, are after all Japanese works of art.

Distances have been shortened due to development of traffic facilities, and international understanding is strongly desired as never before. Oral and written languages are important media for this purpose, but the part borne by the arts, we believe, is no less significant. We sincerely hope that this exhibition, like the previous one, may be visited by a large audience. We are enormously indebted again to the Honolulu Academy of Arts for its generous efforts in making this final showing possible through the through-going cooperation of its Staff.

Nagatake Asano
Director, Tokyo National Museum

February, 1957

序

　1955年私たちはホノルル・アカデミー・オブ・アーツで，第1回の日本美術展覧会を催した。それは長い間懸案になっていたものがようやく実現されたもので，予想以上の成績を収めたことは，今思い出しても愉快なことである。そのため私たちはホノルルが近くなったことを感じたが，またホノルルにおられる方々も日本が一層近くなったと感じておられることと思う。その翌年引きつづいて第2回目の日本美術展覧会を開くのが最初の計画であったが，やむをえぬ事情のため延期しなければならなかったのは残念なことであった。

　しかし今ここに第2回目の展覧会を催すことが出来たことは，1年延期されていただけに一層の喜びを感じる。今度の展覧会は第1回の時には絵画を展観したので，古代から近世に至る彫刻と工芸とを展覧することとした。日本の彫刻は中国の影響を受けたところも多かったが，また日本独特のものも多く示しているのである。殊にその工芸は日本の国民生活の中に生れ育ったものであるから，何よりもよくそれらを通じて日本の文化が理解されることと思う。日本趣味は最近欧米で注目されているようであるが，私たちはそれに迎合せず成るべく広い視野の中で出品物を選出するようにした。そのために日本趣味らしくないものも混じているが，それもまた日本が生んだものと知ってもらいたい。

　交通機関の発達によって距離の短縮された今日，国民相互の理解は一層強く要求されるようになった。そのためには言葉や文字のもつ使命にも大きいものがあるが，また美術の果す役割にも大きいものがあることを信じ，第1回の時のように今次の展覧会もまた多くの人たちによって観覧されることを祈ってやまない。それにつけてもホノルル・アカデミー・オブ・アーツが多くの犠牲を払って，重ねて日本美術展観の機会を与えられたことを，深く感謝する次第である。

　1957年2月

東京国立博物館長　　浅　野　長　武

INTRODUCTION

Sculpture and Decorative Arts of Japan

The Cultural Background of the Pre-Buddhistic Periods

The development of a culture in its nascency is very slow. So it was with the embryonic stage of Japanese culture many hundreds of years ago. The people of the time lived a primitive life, depending chiefly upon hunting and fishing, and their artifacts were mostly implements for use in their daily life. Notable among them in artistic ornamentation was the earthenware known as the Jōmon Type. This earthenware was in use over a long period of time in various parts of the land of Japan, and gave rise to a rich variety of forms. Because specimens of this ware are found in greater quantity in such regions in the eastern half of Japan as the Kantō Plain and the Northeastern District, it is believed that the culture represented by the Jōmon Type of earthenware was especially deeply rooted in these regions.

The Jōmon ("rope pattern or mark") earthenware is characterized by marks on its surface impressed by means of rope. The Period of Culture of the Jōmon Type Earthenware, hereinafter abbreviated as the Jōmon Period, derived its name from this fact. In the middle to the last parts of this period, earthenware pieces were decorated with large sculptural ornaments. From the same clay as these implements, artisans made human and animal figures, which manifest grotesque expressions having much in common with the primitive arts of other parts of the world.

After the long-continued Jōmon Period, Chinese culture of the Han Dynasty was introduced into Japan around the third or second century B. C. by way of the Korean Peninsula. This was a highly developed metallic culture previously unknown in Japan, and it is considered that the art of farming was imported together with this new culture. The metal implements of the time included *dō-ken* (a bronze double-edged sword), *dōboko* (a bronze spear with flat double-edged blade aand short tang inserted into the shaft) and *dō-ka* (a bronze halberd with flat double-edged blade and a cylindrical handle into which the shaft was inserted). Probably some iron implements were also imported. The spread of this new culture caused a changing concept in earthenware as well, for a new type, characterized by a smoother, less decorated and more refined workmanship than the Jōmon Type, made its appearance. This new type is known as Yayoi Type Earthenware from the place where its first specimens were excavated. The period during which this earthenware was in use is called the Period of Culture of the Yayoi Type Earthenware, hereafter referred to for convenience as the Yayoi Period.

It is characteristic of the Yayoi Period that such edged implements as the bronze swords and spears seem to have been used in the western part of Japan, and "bronze bells" in central Japan, while no trace at all the of the use of metal implements has been found in the eastern regions. However, agriculture (rice raising) spread widely throughout the land, and the arts of livelihood were remarkably improved. As rice culture flourished with the passage of time, social construction began to assume different aspects. Small communities made their appearance in different localities, and these gradually merged into larger ones which might be considered small states. These states were eventually to be brought under a single control to form the Japanese nation.

Among these "state communities" there arose a practice, notably in the Kinki District in central Japan, of building huge tumuli in which important persons were buried These burial mounds, which may be described as artificial hills, varied in size, and the practice of building such tumuli gradually became nation-wide. This fact proves that the civilization of the time permeated nearly every part of the Japanese land. Because the culture of this period is best known from the artifacts excavated from these tumuli, the era is known as the Period of Ancient Burial Mounds.

Around the base of the ancient burial mounds were set up terra-cotta cylinders (*haniwa* cylinders), like barrels, to prevent landslide, and on the mounds were placed *haniwa* figures of various type -- male and female human figures, animals such as horses, monkeys and birds, and implements like chairs and desks, as well as models of houses, storehouses and boats. Actual pieces of clothing, armor, weapons and horse-trappings belonging to the dead, and iron carpentry tools and other artifacts, were also placed within the burial chamber. The finds from the burial chambers also contain objects used in rituals for the dead. There are some traces of certain organic substances such as fabrics as well, but extant pieces consist of such mineral substances as metal, jade, glass and crystal. Many of these artifacts are fine works of handicraft. Judging from the finds, the Period of Ancient Burial Mounds extended from about the third to the sixth or seventh centuries A. D.

A new day for Japanese culture dawned when Buddhism was introduced in the middle part of the sixth century. Buddhism introduced statues of a sacred nature to which to pray for public welfare. Grand monasteries were built to house the icons, and the interiors of the buildings were decorated with various kinds of ornament to embellish the rituals. Japanese art – sculpture and decorative arts included -- thereafter evolved a multi-faceted development.

Sculpture

Early examples of plastic arts are to be found in the clay figurines, masks and animal figures of the Jōmon Period and the *haniwa* figures of the Period of Ancient Burial Mounds, but they can hardly be considered as anything more than primitive. Buddhism, introduced in the Asuka Period, caused a marked revolution and progress in

6

all aspects of culture. Sculpture, in the strict sense of the word, actually had its beginnig with Buddhist statues. Early Buddhist sculpture in Japan was derived from the Chinese styles of the Six Dynasties, notably that of the Northern Wei period. Statues of the Asuka Period are characterized by their symmetrical forms designed approximately in isosceles triangles, which are rich in dignified, stylized beauty. These characteristics constitute what is called the Asuka style.

As time went on, the Buddhist faith permeated all classes during the Early Nara or Hakuhō Period, which followed after the passage of a century. Buddhist icons, no longer strange to the Japanese sentiment, began to be rendered with the modest naturalness so characteristic of the Japanese point of view in the arts. China at the time was a large, powerful country under the T'ang Emperors. Japan had frequently sent Imperial messengers to T'ang China, and Chinese scholars and technicians had come across the sea to Japan. The newly introduced national system of T'ang China was soon imitated, and Japan was now flooded with fresh vigor for change. The poses and drapery of Japanese Buddhist statues, where T'ang influence was no doubt at work, were freer, lighter and more realistic. This Hakuhō Style is manifest in the group of gilt-bronze statuettes known as the "Forty-eight Buddhas" (*Shijūhattai-butsu*) originally in the Hōryū-ji in Nara and now kept by the Tokyo National Museum.

The national power of Japan continued to develop in the Late Nara Period. Buddhism prospered under national protection, and numerous monasteries were built in the capital as well as in local districts. The famous Great Buddha, a colossal bronze statue in the Tōdai-ji in Nara, measuring over fifty feet in height, was made in this aspiring period. Besides bronze and wood, plastic materials like clay and dry-lacquer (layers of hemp cloth cemented with lacquer) began to be used for sculpture to enable freer, more realistic representation. The sculpture in the Nara Period was characterized by its polished realism within the realm of Oriental profundity, thus establishing a norm to be followed in later periods.

Due to internal disturbances which took place during the T'ang Dynasty, official international communication was suspended in the first part of the Heian Period. Japanese arts gradually freed themselves from Chinese influence. In sculpture, the realistic representation of details was now boldly omitted in order to emphasize spiritual vigor, which eventually created a different kind of beauty. Clay and dry-lacquer went out of use, and wood became the chief material for sculpture. The tendency towards Japanization was even more advanced in the Late Heian Period, resulting in a modest, quiet effect. Deep, powerful chiselwork gave way to shallow, flowing carving suitable to the warm softness characteristic of the time.

The Kamakura Period, under the rule of the military lords, saw the rise of many distinguished Buddhist sculptors. Discarding the graceful, effeminate beauty so loved by aristocrats of the preceding Heian period, they sought a powerful vigor. Their favorite subjects were figures in vigorous motion, in which they portrayed the muscular strength with remarkable realism. Their sharp, deep carving illustrates the spirit of the "warriors' age". It is only natural that portrait sculpture also should become fashionable in such a realistic period. While statues of humans during the Nara Period usually depicted Buddhist priests, those of the Kamakura Period, on the other hand, reflecting the atmosphere of the time, emphasized secular subjects as well. The statue of Minamoto Yoritomo, founder of the Kamakura military government, is a typical example of this sort.

Buddhist subject matter formed the main current of Japanese sculpture, but masks attract us with a different kind of interest.

Masks

Gigaku masks   The *Gigaku* was a kind of dramatic performance introduced into Japan from China. It was performed very frequently in the Asuka and Nara Periods (seventh to eighth centuries) in public places such as the courtyards of Buddhist monasteries. Masks used in the *Gigaku* are relatively realistic, and are large-sized to cover the whole of the wearers' heads. The oldest of worn masks in Japan, they are of high artistic as well as historical value.

Nō and Kyōgen masks   The *Nō* appears to have evolved from a kind of dramatic play performed from since early times throughout Japan. Given distinction by a distinguished performer around the fourteenth century in the Muromachi Period, and under the patronage of the Ashikaga shoguns who were the administrators of Japan at the time, it developed into a highly polished art. As its performance began to take a longer and longer time, its masks tended to be smaller and lighter. In order to be able to give different expressions of joy and sorrow during the performances, the masks were furnished with "intermediate expressions", which, in conformity with the actions and costumes of the wearers, could convey a variety of feelings.

The *Kyōgen* is a light entertainment played in the interlude between *Nō* dramas. While the *Nō* is of a serious nature and is performed with a slow, elegant dance, the *Kyōgen* is a farce with humorous gesticulation. Masks used in this interlude developed side by side with those for the *Nō*. *Kyōgen* masks are not so rich in variety as *Nō* masks, but they attract us by their interesting expressions cunningly devised to match the farcical presentation of *Kyōgen*.

Decorative Arts

Handicrafts during the primitive periods were mostly implements for practical use. When objects of utility were designed with more and more decorative effects, they became works worthy of artistic appreciation. The Jōmon Type of earthenware may be cited as an example of this sort. Earthenware pieces of this type were made of rough clay, the surface of which was trimmed by rolling a rod wound with rope upon it. This accidental "rope pattern" (*jōmon*) impressed on the surface led in turn to intentional carvings and finally to heavily sculptured ornamentation. Earthenware implements of the Yayoi Type were also primarily designed for utility. We find among them pieces fashioned in light, pleasing shapes, and some are painted with a beautiful red pigment.

The Sue Type of earthenware was fashioned on the potter's wheel, and its body could therefore be thinner. Higher-fired, it is of a harder quality like stoneware, and when beaten it gives a hard, metallic sound. Most of the extant Sue pieces are of unglazed grayish ware, but some have an accidental glaze caused by wood ashes falling on the surface during the firing. The sue technique was probably imported from south Korea in about the sixth century.

The use of metals was introduced from China or the Korean Peninsula. Later on, implements for utility began to be made of iron, and bronze tended to be reserved for making valuables, religious ritual implements, and personal ornaments. The bronze swords and spears with large flat blades, and the bell-shaped bronzes known as *dōtaku* ("bronze bells"), probably had a religious origin. Personal objects consist of crowns, buckles, armlets and bracelets, armor, weapons, mirrors, and horse-trappings. Distinct technical progress can be noted especially in the objects made of pure gold and of gilt bronze openwork.

The Asuka, Nara and Heian were the periods during which Buddhism was most active. Implements for the Buddhist rituals and services, and ornaments to be used in temples, were required in great quantity, and this fact was the most important element in the advancement of handicraft techniques. The mass of the craftsmen in these periods were attached to Buddhist monasteries. Works of art from this age reveal an invigorated spirit in which attempts were made at new types, forms and techniques, inspired by other Far Eastern and even Central Asiatic arts. Specimens of the Asuka and Nara Periods are the oldest of the Japanese cultural heritage handed down through the generations, while those of the previous epochs are all excavated pieces.

The Heian Period saw the rise of a movement for Japanization in the decorative arts. It is an indigenous Japanese tendency in decorative design that such nature-inspired subject matter as the flowers of the four seasons, plants, butterflies, and birds are skillfully conventionalized to match the objects on which they are executed. Tender, noble beauty characterize them. A typical example of the sort is found in the mirror-back design of autumn grasses flowering along a water-stream, with birds and butterflies in flight above. In *maki-e** lacquer, bits of gold and silver leaf of various sizes are scattered

---

* "Sprinkled picture". A design is drawn in liquid lacquer on a lacquered surface, and gold and silver filings are sprinkled over it.

both densely and sparingly to form a design of landscape or flowers-and-birds. Nacre inlay, which enriches the decorative effect with the iridescent sheen of mother-of-pearl, began to come into frequent use in this period.

The Buddhistic and aristocratic arts remained active during the first part of the Kamakura Period. As the warrior class began to rise in power, however, the control of the central government declined. Local powers became influential, and local culture progressed accordingly. The art of making swords and "sword furniture" developed rapidly. An original style of metal carving was originated by a talented craftsman during the Muromachi Period, and his school thereafter fed the main current of "sword furniture" art until the end of the feudal age. Individual cities also gave birth to various local styles of sword guards and furniture.

The *maki-e* art of lacquer has had an uninterrupted progress since the Heian Period. Designs and techniques grew more and more elaborate, and a number of new varieties came into being such as, for example, the *taka* ("high") *maki-e*, with the design raised in low relief and finished on the surface in *maki-e*. The *nashi-ji* ("pear-skin ground" – a ground decoration with particles of gold and silver scattered over a lacquered surface to resemble in effect the aventurine lacquer) appeared in the Edo Period to add to the gorgeousness of the lacquerer's art. Furniture and personal objects of such luxurious lacquer ware were manufactured for the enjoyment of feudal lords and rich merchants. The vogue, in the Edo Period, of *inrō* (medicine caddies carried on waist with string passed through the sash) led to interest in similarly small-sized objects. The same fashion was instrumental in spreading a liking for *netsuke*, pieces of wood or ivory carving fastened on the end of the *inrō* string. Subject matter in *maki-e* design covered a wide variety, such as illustrations of historical or fictitious romances, "auspicious" patterns, warriors in armor, animals, etc. Richness in variety was also to be found on designs of "sword furniture", mirrors and such-like in the Edo Period.

Techniques in the art of textile manufacture had been varied as early as the Nara Period. The vogue of the *Nō* play in the Muromachi Period, which caused the development of the art of mask carving, was instrumental also in bringing about the development of *Nō* costumes. *Nō* robes, typified by the specimens shown here, displayed an extremely luxurious beauty. Remarkable progress was seen also in ordinary clothing. *Kosode*, or clothing with short hanging-sleeves (the origin of the present-day Japanese *kimono*), as well as *uchikake* (a formal outer garment worn over the kimono) and *furisode* (a kimono with long hanging-sleeves), manifested a wide variety of design and color.

Extensive changes took place in ceramic manufacture during the Kamakura Period. At Seto, the traditional light-green glaze of wood-ash quality was replaced by a brownish-yellow one, and the brown or black glaze known as *temmoku* made its appearance. Another important new development was the method of ornamenting the surface with stamped or incised patterns, which was extensively used thereafter. Tokonabe, located near Seto, also became very active in ceramic manufacture at the beginning of the Kamakura Period. Its activity in producing implements for daily use surpassed even that of Seto. Both Seto and Tokonabe wares were more advanced versions of the Sue ware which had been produced in various localities. Other wares along the line of the Sue Type, such as the Bizen, Iga and Shigaraki, only barely maintained their existence.

Ceramics of the Seto group in the following Muromachi and Momoyama Periods gave birth to such unique types as the Shino and Oribe under the guidance of the tea masters, who were great aesthetes. The new approach through the "tea-ceremony taste", characterized by the attitude of finding beauty in artless, imperfect things, led to the unique evolution of later Japanese pottery wares.

Early in the Edo Period, Sakaida Kakiemon in Hizen (now Saga Prefecture in Kyushu) made the first enamelled porcelain in Japan; Nonomura Ninsei in Kyoto created a graceful kind of enamelled pottery which reproduced the elegant beauty of *maki-e* lacquer. Wares of various new kinds came into being after them, leading to the many-sided progress of Japanese ceramics. The techniques and styles of these wares form the undercurrent of ceramic art in present-day Japan.

日 本 の 彫 刻 と 工 芸

日 本 文 化 の 背 景

　文化の発祥の最初の段階では極めて徐々に進歩の歩みが運ばれてきたことは，何処の地域の文明にも見られるように，日本の文明も静かな歩みを以て芽生えた。それは今から数千年の昔に遡る時期であった。その頃の人々は狩猟や漁撈を主とした原始生活を営んでいて，作る器物も生活に必要なものが主であった。その中にあって工芸的な意匠化にすぐれたものを見せたのは縄文土器である。この土器は日本の各地域の広い範囲にわたって長い間行われ，様々の形式を生んだ中でも関東，東北地方など東日本の地域に最も多く見られるので，そこに深く根ざしたあとが窺われる。元々，土器の表面に縄目の圧痕のあるのが特徴で縄文式時代と言う，その時代の文化をあらわす名も，そこから由来したのである。この時代の中期から後期にかけては意匠に浮彫的な大形の装飾が施されるようになり，また土器を作る間に同様の土を以て人体や動物を象ったものを造った。そこには古代人に特有な奇怪な表情の見られるのが特色である。

　縄文式時代が長く続いた後，紀元前二三世紀の頃，中国の漢代の文化が朝鮮半島を経て日本に伝わった。それは日本には全く新しい高度の金属文化であって，農耕の法も共に伝えたものと考えられている。金属文化には銅剣，銅鉾，銅戈などがあり，鉄製器も伴って伝わったと認められている。この新しい文化が行われるにつれて土器にも変化があり，縄文式土器とはちがって，文様の少い，軽快にして明るい感じのある土器が行われ始めた。この土器は，最初発見された土地の地名によって弥生式土器と名づけられている。縄文土器に代って広く行われたので，この時期を弥生式時代と言っている。弥生式時代の特色として，銅剣，銅鉾などの金属製利器は西日本の地域に行われ，近畿地方を中心とする中央部には銅鐸が行われ，東部地域には金属器の形跡が見られないことである。しかし，米を栽培して食料とする農耕生活は広く各地域にゆきわたり，生活は著しく改善された。米穀の収穫が豊かになるにつれて国内の社会の事情も変って，地域的に小さな集団が出来，それが次第に大きな集団に纏りつつ小国家の形を整え，やがて統一ある日本が形成される素地をつくるようになった。

　国家的な集団が形づくられた中でも，近畿地方を中心として指導的な地位にあった者の間には死後，屍を埋葬するに盛土を築いた巨大な高塚墳墓を営む風が起った。高塚墳墓にも勿論大小あるが，これが全国的に営まれる傾向になったのは当時の文化が日本の殆ど全地域に及んだことを物語るものである。そして，この時代の文化の様子を研究し，知るには墳墓の中から出土した遺品の調査によるのが最も便宜である実状から，この時期を古墳時代と呼んでいる。

　古墳時代の墳墓は外形の盛土に埴輪円筒を立て繞らした。その間に男女の形をした埴輪や馬，犬，鳥などの動物の形，椅子や舟などの器具或は家屋の雛形と見られる埴輪を配列し，墓の内部には墓の主の服装品，武器　甲冑，馬具や鉄製工作具類を埋納した。また，死者に対して祭を行った器物も見ることができる。そのうちには繊維製品など有機質のものも認められるが，遺存し

ているのは金属製品，硬玉，水晶，硝子などの礦物質のものが主であるが，そこには古代文化と
しては優れた工芸技術になるものが見られる．これらの遺物によって古墳時代は大体3世紀から
6，7世紀とすることができる．

　6世紀の中頃に仏教が伝わって，日本文化は新しい黎明を迎えた．仏教では大衆の共同の福祉
を希う大規模な寺院を建築し，仏像を祀り，堂塔の内部には法会を行うために華麗に充ちた装飾
品を燦然と輝くまでに飾った．この事は日本の文化に新しい面を開拓した点が少くない．以下
に彫刻と工芸について項をわけて述べる．

彫 刻 小 史

　彫塑的な作例は縄文式時代の土偶や動物形，または古墳に飾った埴輪形象にも見られるが，ま
だ，素朴な域を脱しなかった．飛鳥時代に仏教が伝えられたことは凡ての文化に著しい改変と進
歩を促したのであって，彫刻においても，仏像彫刻が造顕されるに至って観念的にも感覚的にも
純粋な彫刻が製作される気運が醸成されたのである．初期の仏教彫刻は中国の北魏式，あるいは，
六朝様式の流を受けたもので像の姿態は左右に均整のとれた形で荘重な美しさを保ったものであ
る．これを飛鳥様式と言っている．

　一世紀を経過した奈良時代前期（あるいは白鳳時代）になると仏教に対する信仰は朝野に浸潤
し驚異を以て迎えられた仏像にも馴れて日本的な柔和な，そして自由な美を求めるようになった．
その頃，中国は唐の治世となっていて，強大な統一国家をなしていた．日本は唐に使節を派遣し，
国交を通じていて，唐からも学者や技術者が渡来した．その新しい制度を導入して国内の体勢が
改新され，革新の気が溢れていた．この時代の彫刻は唐の影響にもよるが，姿態にも衣紋にも自
由な写実味が加わり，軽快な彫刻が造られるようになった．その作例は，いわゆる四十八体仏と
呼ばれている金銅仏のうちのあるものや，それに類した小仏像のうちにも見られる．

　奈良時代の後期には国力はいよいよ隆昌に赴き，仏教は国家の厚い保護をうけ，都を始め地方
諸地域に寺院が建設されたものが多く，活気に満ちた時期となった．東大寺の大仏が造られたの
はこの時である．また，彫刻の技術も進歩し，金銅や木彫の外に，乾漆，塑土など柔かくて写実
的な表現に適した材料が取入れられた．その写実的な彫刻は堅実味を加え，かつ，東洋的な風格
を備え，永く後世の規範となった．

　平安時代の前期に唐朝の内政が乱れたために公式の通交が停止し一般に日本化の運動が高まっ
た中にあって，彫刻もまた，精神的な力強さを表わすために写実的な表現に対して大胆な省略を
なす一方，新しい美しさを強調する風を生じ，専ら木彫が多く作られるようになった．平安時代
の後期には，ますます，日本化が高まって穏やかさを追うようになって，柔かく暖か味のある平
静な感情を表現するようになった．

　鎌倉時代は傑出した仏師の輩出した時代であって，彼等は優雅な彫刻から脱して活々とした力
強い表現を求め，動的な姿勢をよく捉え，筋肉の動きを巧みに描写した．したがって，彫りを深
く〔し〕て力強さを示そうと試みたのが時代の好みにあったのである．肖像彫刻が法体ではなく俗形

のままの形に作られるようになったのは，この鎌倉時代からのことで時代の要求によるところである。源頼朝像はこの時代の肖像彫刻の代表的な作例である。

　日本の彫刻は仏像彫刻を主流としたが，仮面彫刻にも見るべきものがある。

仮面

　伎楽面——伎楽は中国を経て日本に伝えられた演劇で，飛鳥，奈良時代（7，8世紀）には寺院の広場などで盛んに行われた。伎楽に用いた仮面は写実味に豊んだもので頭部を覆う位に大きく作られている。わが国の仮面のうちでは最も古い遺品で，彫刻技術も優れて仮面としてだけでなく，彫刻史の上にも価値の高いものである。

　能，狂言面——古くから日本の各地方の民衆の間に行われていた歌舞があったが，能楽は室町時代に，傑出した演技者が出て改良を加え，また，当時の為政者たる足利将軍の保護を受け，高級な芸術に発展したのである。能面は能楽の演出に用いられた仮面を言う。能楽に用いられる仮面は演出の時間が長くなるにつれて，仮面を軽く，演出に都合のよいものに工夫されたし，また，長い演出の間に喜びや悲しみの場面の変化にも応じられる工夫から喜びと悲しみの中間の表情に作り，着装の操作による陰影の変化で喜び，あるいは，悲しみの表情を現わすことに工夫された。

　狂言に用いる仮面も能面と同じグループの中で発達したものである。その種類は能面ほど多くないが，喜劇用として巧みに工夫された点は注目に値するものがある。狂言面の形式には自然に人を笑いに誘う表情と矛盾から笑いを呼びおこす滑稽の表情とがある。また，この喜劇に演ぜられる人物は美男美女ではなくて，愚夫，醜女が多いけれども，それが不快な感じを抱かせるものではなくて，人のよい明るさを持っていることは喜劇の本質をよく知るものであり，これが滑稽なために卑俗に見られ易いのであるけれども，演出の効果の上からは喜劇用仮面としての特性を理解して作られている。

工　芸　小　史

　原始工芸品には初め実用品であったものに意匠化が加えられて次第に鑑賞に値する高さにまで発展したものが見られる。縄文土器はこの例であって，粗い粘土で土器を作る際に縄を棒に巻いたもので形を整えるときに出来た文様が基となって遂に派手な大形な模様を作り出すに至ったのである。弥生式土器にも実用品が多いが，その優れたものには軽快な器形で，中には赤い塗料で彩色した美しいものがある。須恵器は縄文，弥生のような手造り式の原始的な土器と違って，轆轤によって造られた器である。したがって，胎造りが薄く，また，焼成する火力が強いため，堅く焼き締り，叩けばチンチンと金属性の音がする。釉のない鼠色肌のものが多いが，中には焼成の際に灰の作用で器表の一部に半透明な黄緑色の釉，いわゆる自然釉のかかったものもある。はやくから，朝鮮地方で焼かれていた方法が六世紀の頃，日本に伝わったと考えられる。

　金属器は中国あるいは朝鮮から伝えたもので，そのうち，実用のものは鉄製品に譲って銅製品は実用を離れた貴重品乃至は宗教的な祭礼品，あるいは，装身具に移って行った。大型の銅鉾，銅鐸などは宗教的な意味を有ったものと考えられている。身体の装飾品や調度類では，冠，帯金

具，腕輪，耳飾，あるいは武器，甲冑の類，鏡，または乗馬の飾などが主なもので，銅の透金具に鍍金を施したものや，純金の細工物には技術の進歩したあとが見られる。

　飛鳥，奈良時代から平安時代に続く時期においては仏教活動が最も旺盛であって，工芸技術の進歩の推進の中心となったものは仏教の法会修法の道具や寺院の装飾調度を調製することにあった。そして工人も多く寺院に属していた。したがって，寺院関係の調度・装飾品に多くの工芸品が見られるのは自然の数である。しかも，仏教活動は独り日本のみでなく，アジア極東諸地域に普及していて，時には盛衰もあったが，互に交流することが少なくなかったので，広い視野の中から新しい技法を得て進歩，改善を加えるものがあった。今日の我々は，飛鳥・奈良時代から後の遺品において初めて地上の宝庫に伝えられた文化の遺産を見ることができるのである。法隆寺や東大寺正倉院に千古の美術工芸品の伝えられていることは普く人々の知るところである。

　平安時代の工芸品の上には日本化の運動が行われていた。日本的な特色は，意匠の上では四季の花・草・蝶・鳥など野外，自然の景観を巧みに図案化して器物に応用したところにある。そこには，やさしく，また，気品の高い情緒があふれている。鏡や漆芸品の図案に，小川の流れに秋草の咲き乱れているところ，一二鳥・蝶の舞う状景を見るのはその例である。漆工芸の蒔絵は日本で育成され，発達した技術で，金銀の大小の粉末を以てあるいは密に，あるいは粗にして花鳥・風景などの図を作っている。青貝を以て光彩の変化による効果をあげた螺鈿装のものもこの時期から漸く多く見られる。

　鎌倉時代の初めには，まだ，仏教的な，貴族的な従来の余風が流れていたけれども，武家の力が強まり，中央政府の政治力が衰えるにつれて，地方では各地に豪族が力を得て，地方文化も進んできた。その間にあって工芸の動向を見ると，武家の愛用する刀の流行とともに刀工が各地に起り，したがって，刀剣の装具を作ることも盛んになり，室町時代には傑れた名工が出て彫金の技法に新機軸を開きその流派は永く後まで，刀装具の基準となった。また，地方各地の都市城下町にも，鐔工・刀装具を作る工人が出でそれぞれ特色ある装具を作った。

　蒔絵もまた，こうした社会の人々の愛好するところで，平安時代以来，一向に衰えず，意匠と技法が益々円熟，複雑化して，平面的な蒔絵から，漆を盛った高蒔絵による新しい方法が考案され豪華の度を加えた。また梨子地蒔が発達して，江戸時代には大名・豪商などの調度とされた。印籠の流行は趣味を小器物の末端にまで馳せたし，その意匠は，山水画というよりは，歴史物語・説話・瑞祥・武者絵・動物など，凡ゆるものに題材を求め親しみ易い面を見せている。このことは，刀装具や鏡の図案などにも共通したところであって，江戸時代の趣味である。

　このような中における一面に染織の興隆がある。能楽の流行は仮面の発達を促したがそれは同時に装束にも及んだのであって能衣裳は実に絢爛たるものが作られた。大名や町家の間には小袖が流行し，機業の発達と相俟って小袖・打掛・振袖には図案の種類も染色の配合も多種多様な変化を見せ着物に対して華やかな面を作った。

　陶器界も鎌倉時代になってから著しい変化が現われた。すなわち瀬戸では従来から行われていた淡緑色の灰質釉は黄茶色に変り，また新たに飴あるいは黒の，いわゆる天目釉が発見された。

さらに型押しや箆彫りの模様を器に表わすことが盛んに行われたのも，見逃し得ない進歩であったといえる。また瀬戸に近い常滑でも，当期の初めから非常に窯業が盛んになり，日用器の焼成では瀬戸を凌ぐほどであった。この瀬戸，常滑陶の発展は前から各地で行われていた須恵器焼成の進歩であったが，その他の須恵系の備前・伊賀・信楽などの陶業は，わずかに命脈を保っていたに過ぎなかった。

この瀬戸窯業は，次の室町・桃山の茶道の流行とともに，優れた茶人たちの指導によって志野・織部のような異色ある器を生んだ。志野や織部のような，不完全な中に美しさを見出す茶的な審美眼は，その後の日本陶器に独自の発展をもたらす基になった。

他方，江戸初期には九州の肥前国の人酒井田柿右衛門による磁器の色絵付が完成され，また京都の野々村仁清は蒔絵の持つ美しさを盛った陶芸を焼成するなど，新様式の陶業が相次いで勃興し，陶器界はすこぶる多彩となった。その流れが現在の日本陶業の基盤となっている。

SCULPTURE

1—15 *Statues*

1. CLAY FIGURINE　　土　　偶

Jōmon Period.

H. 7 ⅛″.　From Saitama-ken.

Most of the clay figurines of the Jōmon Period are relatively small in size, and have a grotesque appearance with extremely large eyes. They are considered to have been used for a religious purpose.

2. CLAY FIGURINE　　土　　偶

Jōmon Period.

H. 14 ⅜″.　From Nagano-ken.

3. HANIWA FIGURE OF A MAN　　埴　輪　男　子

Period of Ancient Burial Mounds.

H. 44 ⅞″.　From Gumma-ken.

Haniwa figures were set up on mounds built over burial chambers. Shown here is a typical example of the most usual form of male figure, with trousers and a sword at the waist.

4. HANIWA FIGURE OF A WOMAN　　埴　輪　女　子

Period of Ancient Burial Mounds.

H. 29 ⅜″.　From Ibaragi-ken.

5. HANIWA FIGURE OF A DOG　　埴　輪　犬

Period of Ancient Burial Mounds.

H. 18 ⅛″.　L. 20 ⅞″.　From Gumma-ken.

As a piece of proto-historic art, this dog is notable for the skillful representation of its face. It illustrates the affectionate feeling with which the proto-historic people regarded their domestic animals.

6. HANIWA MODEL OF A HOUSE　　埴　輪　家

Period of Ancient Burial Mounds.

H. 19 ⅛″.　W. 16 ⅜″.　From Nara-ken.

7. MIROKU BOSATSU　　弥勒菩薩半跏像

Nara Period.

Gilt bronze.　H. 11 ⅜″.

Miroku is the Buddhist Messiah, who is to preside over the "next Buddhist world". The pose of contemplation, seated "half cross-legged" with the right hand touching the cheek, is peculiar to this divinity. This is one of the "Forty-eight Buddhas" originally from the Hōryū-ji Monastery in Nara.

8. MIROKU BOSATSU   弥勒菩薩半跏像

Nara Period.
Gilt bronze. H. 11 ⅞″. From the "sutra mound" at Mt. Nachi.

In the belief that the "last day of the Buddhist world" was close at hand, people in the Heian Period buried copies of sutras (Buddhist scriptures), ritual implements and statuettes underground to transmit to the next world. This statue was discovered in the sutra mound at Nachi in Wakayama Prefecture.

9. JŪICHIMEN KANNON   十一面観音立像

Nara Period.
Gilt bronze. H. 16 ¾″. From the "sutra mound" at Mt. Nachi.

Jūichimen ("Eleven Heads") Kannon is so termed because this manifestation of Kannon has eleven diminutive heads showing expressions of mercy, anger and pleasure surmounted by a head of the Buddha. This form is said to represent Kannon's virtue to lead to Buddhahood (the supreme enlightenment) through various difficulties.

10. TAISHAKU TEN   帝 釈 天 立 像

Heian Period.
Wood. H. 39 ⅜″.

Originally revered in Brahmanism as Indra, this god was assimilated into Buddhism in which he is the protector of the heavenly worlds. The light, flowing drapery of this statue typifies the Late Heian style.

11. JION DAISHI   慈 恩 大 師 坐像

Heian Period.
Wood. H. 11 ⅞″.

Jion Daishi was a Chinese priest in the T'ang Dynasty who established Idealistic Buddhism.

12. DAINICHI NYORAI   大 日 如 来 坐像

Heian Period.
Wood. H. 36 ⅞″. Registered Important Cultural Property.

This Supreme Buddha worshipped in esoteric rites is seated with the mudra (hand-symbol) of wisdom. Together with its elaborate lotus pedestal, it typifies the quiet grace so characteristic of the Late Heian Period.

13. AMIDA NYORAI   阿弥陀如来立像

Kamakura Period.
Wood. H. 38 ⅛″.

Buddhist scriptures tell us that there exists a beautiful paradise in the west. Amida is the lord of this "pure land". According to the Paradise Teaching, one who calls upon this Savior will be reborn in the Western Paradise.

14. MEKIRA TAISHŌ　　迷企羅大将立像

Kamakura Period.
Wood. H. 30 $\frac{1}{2}$″. Registered Important Cultural Property.

Mekira is one of the twelve demigods guarding the Buddha Yakushi. Powerful representation of such figures in vigorous motion was a favorite subject for sculptors of the Kamakura Period.

15. MINAMOTO YORITOMO　　源 頼 朝 坐 像

Kamakura Period.
Wood. H. 35 $\frac{3}{8}$″. Registered Important Cultural Property.

Realism of the Kamakura Period is well typified by this master work showing the founder of the Kamakura military government.

16—26 *Masks*

16. GIGAKU MASK, "RIKISHI"　　伎楽面　　力　　士

Nara Period.
Wood. H. 15 $\frac{3}{8}$″. W. 9″.

Used for the role of a powerful muscular guardian, this mask with real beard vividly describes its subject.

17. NŌ MASK, "ŌMI ONNA"　　能面　　近 江 女

Muromachi Period.
Wood. H. 8 $\frac{1}{8}$″. W. 5 $\frac{1}{4}$″.

This mask representing a young lady is used for the role of the heroine in certain *Nō* dramas.

18. NŌ MASK, "WARAI JŌ"　　能面　　笑　　尉

Muromachi Period.
Wood. H. 8″. W. 6 $\frac{3}{8}$″.

Used for the role of a deity in his manifestation as an old man.

19. NŌ MASK, "WAKA OTOKO"　　能面　　若　　男

Momoyama Period.
Wood. H. 7 $\frac{7}{8}$″. W. 5 $\frac{5}{8}$″.

Used for the role of a young man.

20. NŌ MASK, "FUKAI"　　能面　　深　　井

Edo Period.
Wood. H. 8 $\frac{3}{4}$″. W. 5 $\frac{1}{2}$″.

The character of a middle-aged woman is well illustrated by this mask revealing traces of her sad experiences of life.

21. NŌ MASK, "DŌJI"   能面　童　子

Edo Period.
Wood. H. 8 $\frac{1}{8}$″. W. 5 $\frac{1}{2}$″.

Used for the role of a boy.

22. NŌ MASK, "SHIKAMI"   能面　顰　見

Edo Period.
Wood. H. 8 $\frac{3}{8}$″. W. 6 $\frac{1}{8}$″.

Used for the role of a malicious spirit.

23. NŌ MASK, "BESHIMI AKUJŌ"   能面　瘲見悪尉

Edo Period.
Wood. H. 9″. W. 6 $\frac{3}{4}$″.

Showing a terrifying appearance with a twisted mouth and staring eyes, this represents the character of a vengeful spirit.

24. KYŌGEN MASK, "USOBUKI"   狂言面　ウソブキ

Muromachi Period.
Wood. H. 7 $\frac{1}{4}$″. W. 5 $\frac{5}{8}$″.

This amusing mask with a protruding mouth is used for the role of a foolish man as well as for that of spirits of a cicada, an octopus and others.

25. KYŌGEN MASK, "BU-AKU"   狂言面　武　悪

Momoyama Period.
Wood. H. 7 $\frac{1}{2}$″. W. 6 $\frac{7}{8}$″.

This is a travesty of the *Nō* mask "Beshimi". Although used for the role of a goblin, it is more humorous than dreadful.

26. KYŌGEN MASK, "SITAKIRI HIME"   狂言面　舌切姫

Edo Period.
Wood. H. 8 $\frac{1}{8}$″. W. 6 $\frac{1}{8}$″.

Used for the role of an ugly, good-natured woman.

DECORATIVE ARTS

27. SPEAR HEAD 銅　鉾

Yayoi Period.
Bronze. L. 34 ¼″. W. 5 ⅛″. From Nagasaki-ken.

Pre-historic bronze spears termed *dōboko* were originally weapons, but existing specimens have flat wide blades ill adapted for actual use on the battlefield. They were used in the western part of Japan, probably as treasures symbolizing the power and dignity of local clans. The same can be said of the halberd (*dōka*), No. 29.

28. SPEAR HEAD 銅　鉾

Yayoi Period.
Bronze. L. 32 ¼″. W. 3 ⅛″. From Nagasaki-ken.

29. HALBERD 銅　戈

Yayoi Period.
Bronze. L. 11 ⅜″. W. 3 ⅜″. From Wakayama-ken.

30. IMPLEMENT IN THE SHAPE OF A BELL 流水模様銅鐸

Yayoi Period.
Bronze. H. 17 ⅞″. W. 11 ¾″. From Hyogo-ken.

The origin of the *dōtaku* ("bronze bell") is probably to be found in a musical instrument with a clapper hung inside. Most of such bell-shaped bronzes, however, are considered to have been used for ceremonial purposes. Chief among the designs found on them are "water streams" and "crossing bands" cast in relief. This is a specimen of the former group.

31. IMPLEMENT IN THE SHAPE OF A BELL 袈裟襷模様銅鐸

Yayoi Period.
Bronze. H. 31 ⅞″. W. 17 ⅝″.

This is a specimen found at the easternmost location. Its "crossing bands" design cast in relatively high relief suggests that it dates from the latter part of the Yayoi Period.

32. BRACELET WITH BELLS 銅鈴釧

Period of Ancient Burial Mounds.
Bronze. D. 4 ⅜″. From Kagawa-ken.

Ancient Burial Mounds have yielded numerous specimens of personal ornaments such as bracelets, ear-rings and beads of various materials. They attest to the high progress of handicraft techniques in this proto-historic age.

33. BRACELET 石　釧

Period of Ancient Burial Mounds.
Stone. D. 2 ⅞″. From Osaka-fu.

34. BRACELET 石 釧

Period of Ancient Burial Mounds.
Stone. D. 3 ½″. From Kyoto-fu.

35. BLACELET IN THE SHAPE OF A SPADE BLADE 鍬 形 石

Period of Ancient Burial Mounds.
Stone. L. 7 ⅜″. From Kyoto-ku.

36. PAIR OF EAR-RINGS 金 製 耳 飾

Period of Ancient Burial Mounds.
Gold. L. 6 ½″ each. From Kumamoto-ken.

The elaborate workmanship seen in these ear-rings is proof enough of technical achievement in the remote past.

37. PAIR OF EAR-RINGS 金 製 耳 飾

Period of Ancient Burial Mounds.
Gold. L. 2 ½″ each. From Shiga-ken.

38. MAGA-TAMA 勾 玉

Period of Ancient Burial Mounds.
Jade. L. ⅞″. From Kagawa-ken.

Maga-tama ("curving beads"), shaped like commas or claws, are pecular to Japan. Like other contemporary beads they were laced for use as pendent ornaments such as necklaces.

39. MAGA-TAMA 勾 玉

Period of Ancient Burial Mounds.
Jade. L. 1″. From Kagawa-ken.

40. MAGA-TAMA 勾 玉

Period of Ancient Burial Monuds.
Jade. L. 2 ⅛″. Place of excavation unknown.

41. MAGA-TAMA 勾 玉

Period of Ancient Burial Mounds.
Agate. L. 1 ⅞″. From Shimane-ken.

42. MAGA-TAMA 勾 玉

Period of Ancient Burial Mounds.
Jasper. L. 1 ⅝″. From Hyogo-ken.

43. CINERARY URN   金 銅 壺

Nara Period.
Gilt bronze. H. 6 ¾″.

After the introduction of Buddhism, there arose the practice of cremating the dead and burying the ashes in urns. Cinerary urns were more frequently made of pottery, but a few specimens of gilt bronze exist.

44. BUDDHIST RITUAL VASE   銅 水 瓶

Nara Period.
Bronze. H. 9 ⅛″.

45. HEAD OF A SHAKUJŌ   錫 杖 頭

Nara Period.
Bronze. L. of head 7 ⅛″.

The *shakujō* ("pewter staff") is a long staff with sounding rings, used in Buddhist rituals or carried by travelling monks. The sound of a *shakujō* was believed to have the power of keeping away evil spirits.

46. BUDDHIST RITUAL BELL   八仏浮彫五鈷鈴

Heian Period.
Gilt bronze. H. 7 ¼″. Registered Important Cultural Property.

This bell has a handle in the shape of a "five-pronged pestle", which in itself is an exorcising implement in esoteric rites. It is ornamented with a design of eight Sanskrit monograms representing the Eight Buddhas, and bands of floral and circular patterns above and below. The entire surface is gold- and silver-plated. This is among the most ornate of the Buddhist ritual implements.

47. K E I   蓮 池 模 様 磬

Heian Period.
Bronze. Design of lotus pond. L. 3 ⅛″. Registered Important Cultural Property.

The *kei* is a flat gong, shaped more or less like a chevron, used in Buddhist services. This specimen is notable for its fine design.

48. K E I   孔 雀 模 様 磬

Kamakura Period.
Bronze. Design of peacocks. L. 3 ⅝″.

49. SUE-BAKO   竜 模 様 居 箱

Kamakura Period.
Gilt bronze. Design of dragons. L. 8″. W. 13 ⅝″. H. 4 ⅛″.

A *sue-bako* is a box for sermon manuscripts and other objects used in Buddhist rituals.

50. HANGING LANTERN　　梅竹透模様釣燈籠

Muromachi Period.
Bronze, with openwork. Design of prunus trees and bamboos. H. 12 ⅛″. Registered Important Cultural Property.

The fact that this hexagonal lantern in beautiful openwork was finished in only one casting (excepting a panel serving as the door of the fire-chamber) attests to the elaborate metal-work technique achieved in the Muromachi Period. It has an incised inscription to the effect that it was made as a donation to the Chiba-dera Temple in Shimōsa Province (now Chiba Prefecture) on July 28, 1550.

51. DRAGON HEAD　　竜　　頭

Muromachi Period.
Bronze. H. 11 ¾″.

Used as a top ornament on a banner pole.

52. TEA-CEREMONY KETTLE　　茶釜　銘　園城寺

Muromachi Period.
Iron. Design of embossed dots. H. 7 ½″. D. of body 10 ¾″.

Ashiya in Fukuoka Prefecture (Kyushu) is famous for kettles for use in the tea-ceremony. Exhibited here is a typical specimen of an Ashiya kettle, originally in the possession of Matsudaira Fumai, lord of the Matsue Castle and a distinguished tea master.

53. TEA-CEREMONY KETTLE　　茶　　釜

Momoyama Period.
Iron. H. 6 ⅜″. D. of body 10 ⅞″.

54—67　Mirrors

54. MIRROR　　二神二獣模様鏡

Period of Ancient Burial Mounds.
Bronze. Design of two deites and two animals. D. 8 ¼″. From Shizuoka-ken.

This is an imported Chinese mirror dating from the third century. The design on its back shows two Taoistic immortals, and a dragon and a tiger which are their messengers.

55. MIRROR　　鼉竜模様鏡

Period of Ancient Burial Mounds.
Bronze. Design of dragons. D. 17 ⅞″. From Yamaguchi-ken.

The design on the back of this mirror shows *daryū*, dragon-serpents with hard scales, which were fashionable in Chinese art around the third to fourth centuries. This piece is a Japanese work inspired by a Chinese mirror.

56. MIRROR WITH BELLS　　七　鈴　鏡

Period of Ancient Burial Mounds.
Bronze. D. including bells 5 ¼″. Said to be from Gumma-ken.

Mirrors with bells around their rims are exclusively peculiar to Japan.

57. EIGHT- FOLIATE MIRROR　瑞花鳳凰模様八稜鏡
鏡面に蔵王権現像の毛彫がある

Heian Period.
Bronze. Design of *hōsōge* flowers and phoenixes. D. 9 ¼″.

Hōsōge shown on the back of this mirror are imaginary peony-like flowers frequently used as motifs of decorative designs in the Orient. The obverse side of the mirror has an image of the god Zaō Gongen in fine hair-line engraving.

58. MIRROR　秋草蝶鳥模様鏡

Heian Period.
Bronze. Design of autumn grasses, birds and butterflies. D. 3 ⅞″.

59. MIRROR　松枝双鶴模様鏡

Heian Period.
Bronze. Design of pine sprays and two cranes. D. 4 ⅞″.

60. EIGHT-FOLIATE MIRROR　瑞花鴛鴦模様八稜鏡

Heian Period.
Bronze. Design of "auspicious" flowers and mandarin ducks. D. 5 ⅛″.

61. FIVE-LOBED MIRROR　瑞花鴛鴦模様五花鏡

Kamakura Period.
Bronze. Design of "auspicious flowers" and mandarin ducks. D. 4 ½″.

62. MIRROR　甜瓜蝶鳥模様鏡

Kamakura Period.
Bronze. Design of melon, birds and butterflies. D. 4 ⅝″.

63. MIRROR　菊花蝶鳥模様鏡

Kamakura Period.
Bronze. Design of chrysanthemums, birds and butterflies. D. 4 ⅝″.

64. MIRROR　橘樹双鶴模様鏡

Muromachi Period.
Bronze. Design of mandarin-orange trees and two cranes. D. 7 ⅞″.

65. CHAMFERED SQUARE MIRROR　菊桐模様角切方鏡

Momoyama Period.
Bronze. Design of chrysanthemum and paulownia crests. 7 ⅛″ square.

66. MIRROR WITH HANDLE　菊花模様柄鏡

Edo Period.
Bronze. Design of chrysanthemum flowers. D. 5 ⅜″.

67. MIRROR WITH HANDLE   葡萄棚模様柄鏡

Edo Period.

Bronze. Design of a vineyard. D. 4 $\frac{3}{8}$″.

68. ARMOR OF GUSOKU TYPE   二枚胴具足

Momoyama Period.

H. from shoulder down, 31 $\frac{3}{8}$″.

 Gusoku ("complete with all parts") is a term reserved for a type of armor consisting of a helmet, armor, shoulder-pieces, gauntlets, cheek plates, throat protector, and gaiters. The specimen exhibited here, characterized by its beautiful lacing, was used by the military general and great tea master, Kobori Enshū.

69—87   *Sword mountings and accessories*

69. SWORD MOUNTING OF HYŌGO-GUSARI TYPE   三鱗模様兵庫鎖太刀

Kamakura Period.

Silver. Design of triangle diaper in gold-plating. L. 44 $\frac{1}{2}$″. Registered Important Cultural Property.

 Swords kept in the governmental weapon repository (*hyōgo*) were *tachi* (see No. 70) hung from the sash with chains (*kusari*). Shown here is a particularly gorgeous specimen.

70. SWORD-MOUNTING OF KAZA-TACHI TYPE   赤木螺鈿飾太刀

Muromachi Period.

Red sandalwood, with mother-of-pearl inlay and gold ornaments. L. 35 $\frac{7}{8}$″.

 A *tachi* is a sword with a curving blade, worn hung with cords from the sash with the cutting edge downward. A *kaza* (ornamental) *tachi* is for ceremonial use by the nobility.

71. SWORD MOUNTING OF KOSHI-GATANA TYPE   牡丹浮模様腰刀

Muromachi Period.

Wood, with gilt bronze overlay in relief. Design of peonies. L. 15″.

 A *koshi-gatana* is a short sword worn on the waist in addition to a *tachi*. The present specimen, made to order in the district inhabited by the Ainus, is notable for its form, which is somewhat different from the ordinary one.

72. SWORD MOUNTING OF UCHI-GATANA TYPE   黒漆薫革打刀拵

Momoyama Period.

Scabbard, wood, black-lacquered. Handle, wrapped with stained hide. With ornaments of gilt bronze. L. 46 $\frac{3}{4}$″. Registered Important Cultural Property.

 The *uchi-gatana*, otherwise simply called *katana*, denotes that type of sword which is worn thrust through the sash with the cutting edge upward.

73. SWORD MOUNTING OF ITOMAKI-NO-TACHI TYPE   糸巻太刀拵

Edo Period.

Wood, gold-lacquered, with *maki-e* and sheet-metal embedding. L. 45″.

 Ito-maki means "wrapped with braids". This also is a ceremonial type.

74. SWORD MOUNTINGS FOR DAI-SHŌ   黒蠟色刻鞘大小拵

Edo Period.

Wood, incised with diagonal lines and black-lacquered. L.: longer *katana*, 37 ½″; shorter *katana*, 26 ¼″.

Samurai (warriors) in the feudal period used to wear a pair of *katana*, one longer (*dai*) and the other shorter (*shō*).

75. SWORD GUARD   蟹透模様鐔

Muromachi Period.

"Owari Openwork" style. Iron, with openwork. Design of crab. D. (longer, i. e. vertical, measurement; same with the following guards) 3 ⅜″.

A sword guard (*tsuba*) is a flat metal disk fitted in between the blade and the handle to protect the hand. Guards in the Muromachi Period were made by armorers, but later on specialists worked in various districts each in his original style.

76. SWORD GUARD   二ツ巴透模様鐔

Muromachi Period.

"Ko (Old) Shō-ami" style. Iron, with openwork and inlay. Design of *futatsu-domoe* (circle composed of two comma-shapes). D. 3 ⅛″.

The Old Shō-ami School was active in Kyoto towards the end of the Muromachi Period. Old Shō-ami guards are round and made of iron, mostly with simple perforated and inlaid designs.

77. SWORD GUARD   野晒図鐔

By Kane-ie. Muromachi Period.

Iron, with openwork. Design of a skull lying in a field. D. 3 ¼″.

Kane-ie, a famous guard maker during the Muromachi Period in Kyoto, was skilled especially in graphic designs.

78. SWORD GUARD   八ツ蕨手透模様鐔

By Hayashi Matashichi. Momoyama Period.

Iron, with openwork and gold inlay. Design of "fern fronds". D. 3 ⅛″.

The Hayashi School (otherwise known as the Kasuga School) was founded by Matashichi in Higo Province, now Kumamoto Prefecture, in Kyushu. He was unsurpassed in his time in design and in the skill of his openwork and hammering.

79. SWORD GUARD   猛禽捕猿図鐔

By Shimizu Jingo. Momoyama Period.

Iron, with brass inlay. Design of an eagle catching a monkey. D. 3 ⅛″.

Jingo, active at Yatsushiro in Higo, distinguished himself in inlay work.

80. SWORD GUARD   文　字　鐔

By Yasuchika. Edo Period

Iron, with relief carving. Design of characters. D. 3 ½″.

Tsuchiya Yasuchika, born in Yamagata and active in Edo (now Tokyo), was a versatile man, almost unexcelled before and after his time in his masterly command of all materials, designs and techniques.

81. SWORD GUARD   木 賊 刈 図 鐔

By Tō-u. Edo Period.
Iron, with *iro-e* and openwork. Design of a man collecting scouring-rushes. D. 3 ⅛″.

Tō-u was the name used by Yasuchika in his late years. *Iro-e* ("colored picture") means inlay of metals of various colors over relief carving. The same term, when used in ceramics, means over-glaze enamelling.

82. SWORD GUARD   雪花模様散七宝鐔

By Hirata Harunari. Edo Period.
Silver, with cloisonné over gold bed. Design of snow crystals. D. 2 ¾″.

The beautiful transparent cloisonné work of Japan was established probably during the Momoyama Period by Hirata Dōjin. Harunari, active in Edo, was the master of the Hirata School in its eighth generation.

83. SWORD GUARDS FOR DAI-SHŌ   狗児図大小鐔

By Someya Tomonobu. Edo Period.
Iron, with relief carving. Design of puppies. D.: larger guard, 3″; smaller guard, 2 ⅞″.

Tomonobu from Ise Province studied painting in Edo under the famous painter Tani Bunchō. His specialty was brass guards with landscape designs in low relief and colorful inlay. Shown here is a rare specimen of iron in high relief.

84. SWORD GUARD   鯉 図 鐔

By Kanō Natsuo. Edo Period.
Iron, with relief carving and inlay. Design of carp. D. 3 ⅜″.

Natsuo (1828—1898) was the last master of the art of *tsuba*. His favorite material was iron, on which he displayed his great talent in relief and engraving.

85. MITOKORO-MONO   藻草に貝模様三所物

By Gotō Shōjō. Muromachi Period.
Shakudō (black alloy of copper and gold), with relief carving and *iro-e*. Design of acquatic weeds and shellfishes. L. of *kozuka* 3 ¾″. L. of *kōgai* 3 ¾″.

Mitokoro-mono ("three-part set") is a set of "sword furniture" consisting of a *kozuka* (a knife worn in the scabbard), a *kōgai* (a sort of hair-pin also worn in the scabbard), and a pair of *menuki* (ornamental covers on the heads of the rivet which secures the tang in the handle).

86. MITOKORO-MONO   獅子図三所物

By Gotō Tokujō. Momoyama Period.
Shakudō, with relief carving and *iro-e*. Design of lions. L. of *kozuka* 3 ⅞″. L. of *kōgai* 3 ⅜″.

The Gotō Family served the shoguns from the Muromachi to Edo Periods in sixteen successive generations to dominate the art of metal work in Japan. This school specialized in making "sword furniture" pieces, chiefly of *shakudō* and gold or silver.

87. **MITOKORO-MONO**　　十二支図三所物

By Gotō Mitsutaka. Edo Period.
Shakudō, with relief carving and *iro-e*. Design of *jūni-shi* (so-called Twelve Zodiac Animals). L. of
kozuka 3 $\frac{7}{8}$″. L. of *kōgai* 8 $\frac{3}{8}$″.

88—95　Horse trappings

88. **SADDLE**　　萩模様螺鈿鞍

Heian Period.
Wood, lacquered, with mother-of-pearl inlay. Design of bush-clover. H. of pommel 10 $\frac{3}{8}$″. H. of
cantle 13″. L. of seat bars 17 $\frac{3}{8}$″.

　　Saddles in early Japan betrayed Chinese influence, but in the Heian Period they began to have a
more purely Japanese form. They were made of wood, lacquered, and decorated beautifully with *maki-e*
and mother-of-pearl inlay. Exhibited here is a graceful specimen with nacre design of bush-clover (*hagi*).

89. **SADDLE AND STIRRUPS**　　藤模様蒔絵鞍及鐙

Edo Period.
Wood, lacquered, with *maki-e*. Design of wistaria. Saddle: h. of pommel 10 $\frac{5}{8}$″; h. of cantle 10 $\frac{1}{4}$″;
l. of seat bars 12″. L. of stirrups 11 $\frac{5}{8}$″ each.

　　The wistaria designs in *maki-e* of gold and silver present an exquisite color contrast with the black-
lacquered ground of this saddle and its accompanying stirrups.

90. **GYŌYŌ**　　杏　葉

Period of Ancient Burial Mounds.
Gilt bronze. D. 3 $\frac{7}{8}$″. From Shizuoka-ken.

　　In proto-historic trappings, metal-work pendant ornaments were hung on the leather straps passed
around the horse's breast and hips. A *gyōyō* ("ginko-tree leaf"), so termed after the shape, is the one
attached at the hip.

91. **GYŌYŌ**　　杏　葉

Period of Ancient Burial Mounds.
Gilt bronze. D. 6 $\frac{7}{8}$″. From Saitama-ken.

92. **HORSE BELL**　　馬　鐸

Period of Ancient Burial Mounds.
Bronze. L. 6″. From Shizuoka-ken.

93. **HORSE BELL**　　馬　鐸

Period of Ancient Burial Mounds.
Bronze. L. 4 $\frac{7}{8}$″. From Gumma-ken.

94. **HORSE BELL**　　馬　鈴

Period of Ancient Burial Mounds.
Bronze. H. 4 $\frac{7}{8}$″. From Yamaguchi-ken.

95. PAIR OF STIRRUPS   壺　　鐙

Period of Ancient Burial Mounds.
Bronze. H. 7 $\frac{3}{4}''$ each. From Yamaguchi-ken.

96. TEBAKO   千鳥模様蒔絵手箱

Kamakura Period.
Wood, lacquered, with *maki-e*. Design of plovers. L. 10 $\frac{1}{8}''$. W. 13 $\frac{5}{8}''$. H. 7 $\frac{1}{2}''$.

Tebako ("hand box") is a term used in early times to mean a box for a cosmetic set. The present piece is a representative work of *maki-e* lacquer of the Kamakura Period.

97. INCENSE CONTAINER   花鳥模様蒔絵香合

Kamakura Period.
Wood, lacquered, with *maki-e*. Design of flowers-and-birds. L. 3 $\frac{1}{2}''$. W. 2 $\frac{5}{8}''$. H. 1 $\frac{3}{8}''$.

This is a box for containing fragments of incense wood. It is decorated over a thick lacquer coating with designs of birds in embedded sheet silver and flowers in gold *maki-e*.

98. TEBAKO   扇面散模様蒔絵手箱

Muromachi Period.
Wood, lacquered, with *maki-e*. Design of fans. L. 8 $\frac{7}{8}''$. W. 11 $\frac{3}{4}''$. H. 5 $\frac{3}{4}''$. Registered Important Cultural Property.

The beauty of *taka maki-e*, a method of raising a design in low relief and decorating the surface with *maki-e*, is well represented in this fine work with a design of fans showing landscape and flower paintings. "Scattered fans" was one of the motifs popular in decorative designs from the Kamakura times, but here it is presented in the relief *maki-e* technique which was still a novelty at the time.

99. MIRROR BOX   獅子模様蒔絵鏡箱

Muromachi Period.
Wood, lacquered, with *maki-e*. Design of *shishi* (imaginary lion-like animal). D. 8 $\frac{5}{8}''$. H. 2''.

100. INCENSE CABINET   秋草模様蒔絵香箪笥

Momoyama Period.
Wood, lacquered, with *maki-e*. Design of autumn grasses. L. 7 $\frac{5}{8}''$. W. 9''. H. 7 $\frac{3}{4}''$.

This is a box with drawers inside to contain various kinds of incense wood, with a ring handle for convenience in carrying. Its design of flowering plants in autumn, with areas of haze hovering above, shows the innate Japanese love of nature.

101. SUTRA BOX   蓮池模様蒔絵崩経箱

Momoyama Period.
Wood, lacquered, with *maki-e*. Design of a lotus pond. L. 13''. W. 7 $\frac{3}{4}''$. H. 6 $\frac{7}{8}''$.

This box for sutra (Buddhist scripture) is of a rare form: its cover and sides may be opened flat on hinges to facilitate removing the sutra. The lotus is a favorite subject for Buddhist designs.

102. DESK AND INKSTONE-BOX   蔦の細道，角田川模様蒔絵文台及硯箱

By Tatsuke Chōbei. Edo Period.
Wood, lacquered, with *maki-e*. Designs of the River Sumida and "Ivy-bound Lane". Desk: l. 9 $\frac{3}{4}$";
w. 24"; h. 4". Inkstone-box: l. 9 $\frac{1}{4}$"; w. 9"; h. 2".

The *bundai* (low desk for books, writing-paper, etc.) and the *suzuri-bako* (box containing an
inkstone, ink cake, writing brushes, etc.) were indispensable pieces of writing equipment in the past.
The designs on the specimens exhibited are illustrations of old poems. The maker, Tatsuke Chōbei,
was a famous *maki-e* artist in the middle part of the Edo Period.

103. TOOTH-STAIN SET IN BOX   竹菱葵模様蒔絵歯黒箱

Edo Period.
Wood, lacquered, with *maki-e*. Design of hollyhock and bamboo-lozenge crests. Box: l. 6 $\frac{1}{2}$"; w. 6 $\frac{3}{8}$";
h. 6 $\frac{1}{8}$".

Married women in the Edo Period used to stain their teeth black with iron oxide. The set shown
here is from an enormous group of personal objects made for Toyo-hime, daughter of lord Tokugawa
Harutomi of Kii Province, at her wedding. It is a gorgeous collection of *maki-e* work in gold and silver,
still remaining as a complete set.

104. MIRROR RACK   竹菱葵模様蒔絵鏡台

Edo Period.
Wood, lacquered, with *maki-e*. Design of hollyhock and bamboo-lozenge crests. H. 24 $\frac{5}{8}$".

This is another portion of the set made for Toyo-hime. It is a complete set consisting of a mirror,
razor box, cosmetic boxes, combs and other pieces.

105. TRAYS (3 *pieces*)   人物図漆絵膳

Edo Period.
Wood, lacquered, with painting in colored lacquer. 22 $\frac{7}{8}$" square each.

The designs on the lacquered surface of these trays are painted in lacquer blended with red, yellow
and green pigments. "Color lacquer painting" was popular for the decoration of tableware among commoners in the Edo Period.

106—111 Inrō

An *inrō* is a small medicine case carried at the waist by a string passed between the sash and the
clothing. The string has a bead called *ojime* near its middle for adjusting it, and a button or catch termed
netsuke fastened on its other end. Coming into wide use from about the eighteenth century chiefly among
the samurai, *inrō* were made in various techniques, the mass of them being works in *maki-e* or mother-of-
pearl inlay.

106. INRŌ   鳴蟬模様蒔絵印籠

By Koma Kansai. Edo Period.
Wood, lacquered, with *maki-e*. Design of cicada. H. 2 $\frac{1}{2}$". W. 1 $\frac{1}{2}$".

107. INRŌ   放馬模様蒔絵印籠

By Yamada Jōka. Edo Period.
Wood, lacquered, with *maki-e*. Design of horses. H. 3 $\frac{7}{8}$". W. 2".

31

108. INRŌ　鳳凰模様青貝絵印籠

By Somata. Edo Period.
Wood, lacquered, with mother-of-pearl inlay. Design of rounded phoenix. H. 2 $\frac{7}{8}$″. W. 1 $\frac{7}{8}$″.

109. INRŌ　鶏模様蒔絵印籠

Edo Period.
Cloisonné. Design of a cock. H. 2 $\frac{1}{2}$″. W. 2 $\frac{1}{8}$″.

110. INRŌ　畳紙模様蒔絵印籠

By Hasegawa Jūbi (alias Shigeyoshi). Edo Period.
Wood, lacquered, with *maki-e*. Design of folded paper. H. 2 $\frac{3}{4}$″. W. 1 $\frac{1}{2}$″.

111. INRŌ　芦雁模様蒔絵印籠

By Iizuka Tōyō (alias Kanshōsai). Edo Period.
Wood, lacquered, with *maki-e*. Design of wild-geese and reeds. H. 3 $\frac{1}{4}$″. W. 2 $\frac{3}{4}$″.

112—140　Netsuke

Netsuke, attached to *inrō*, are small-sized ornaments serving as their catches, of wood or ivory carving or sometimes made of metal or pottery. Their designs extend over a rich variety of subject matters such as human figures, animals and implements. Executed in elaborate workmanship, they are known throughout the world as a characteristic miniature art of Japan. The middle part of the Edo Period (around the eighteenth century), in particular, gave birth to numerous fine craftsmen in this field.

112. NETSUKE　根付　蝦蟇仙人

By Yoshimura Shūzan. Edo Period.
Wood. Design of Gama Sennin (a Taoistic immortal). H. 4 $\frac{1}{8}$″.

113. NETSUKE　根付　黒　人

Maker unknown. Edo Period.
Wood. Design of a negro. H. 1 $\frac{1}{2}$″.

Black slaves, who came to Japan with the Westerners, aroused curiosity among the Japanese of the feudal age.

114. NETSUKE　根付　烏天狗

By Chokusai. Edo Period.
Ivory. Design of Karasu Tengu. H. 5 $\frac{1}{2}$″.

Karasu Tengu are winged goblins living in mountains, with projecting mouths like beaks of the crow (*karasu*).

115. NETSUKE　根付　白蔵主

By Ogasawara Issai. Edo Period.
Wood. Design of Hakuzōsu (a fox disguised as a Buddhist monk). H. 3 $\frac{1}{4}$″.

116. NETSUKE 根付 手長人物

Maker unknown. Edo Period.
Wood. Design of a man with long arms. H. 3 $\frac{7}{8}$″.

Stories about the lands of "long-arms" and "long-legs" are told in various legends of Japan.

117. NETSUKE 根付 按 摩

By Minkō. Edo Period.
Wood. Design of a blind man. H. 1 $\frac{1}{4}$″.

Many blind men in Japan work as masseurs. *Netsuke* derive interesting subjects from them regarding their ability to detect things which ordinary men cannot see, their fight with canes (as a satire on ignorant people holding power), etc.

118. NETSUKE 根付 熊

By Kaigyokusai. Edo Period.
Ivory. Design of a bear. H. 1 $\frac{1}{4}$″.

119. NETSUKE 根付 山 姥

By Ogasawara Issai. Edo Period.
Wood. Design of *yama-uba*. H. 3 $\frac{3}{8}$″.

Yama-uba are witches living in mountains. The tale of a *yama-uba* who raised the infant Kintarō, later the heroic warrior Sakata Kintoki in the Heian Period, is well known to Japanese children.

120. NETSUKE 根付 猿 廻 し

Maker unknown. Edo Period.
Wood. Design of a monkey leader. H. 2″.

121. NETSUKE 根付 馬上関羽

By Yoshimura Shūzan. Edo Period.
Wood. Design of Kan-u. H. 3 $\frac{3}{8}$″.

Kan-u (in Chinese: Kuan Yü) was a military general in the Period of Three Kingdoms, famous for his enormous strength, devoted loyalty, and long beard, deified in China as a god of warriors.

122. NETSUKE 根付 竜 仙 人

By Yoshimura Shūzan. Edo Period.
Wood. Design of Ryū Sennin (a Taoistic immortal). H. 3 $\frac{7}{8}$″.

123. NETSUKE 根付 紅 葉 狩

By Miwa. Edo Period.
Wood. Design of *momiji-gari* (the story of a warrior fighting with a female goblin). H. 1 $\frac{1}{4}$″.

124. NETSUKE　　根付　紅葉狩

By Jugyoku.　Edo Period.
Wood.　Design of *momiji-gari*.　H. 1 $\frac{3}{8}''$.

125. NETSUKE　　根付　猿廻し

By Miwa.　Edo Period.
Wood.　Design of a monkey leader.　H. 1 $\frac{1}{4}''$.

126. NETSUKE　　根付　傀儡師

By Miwa　Edo Period.
Wood.　Design of a puppeteer.　H. 1 $\frac{1}{4}''$.

127. NETSUKE　　根付　牛

By Miwa.　Edo Period.
Wood.　Design of an ox.　H. 1 $\frac{5}{8}''$.

128. NETSUKE　　根付　犬

By Miwa.　Edo Period.
Wood.　Design of a dog.　D. 1 $\frac{7}{8}''$.

129. NETSUKE　　根付　按　摩

By Miwa.　Edo Period.
Wood.　Design of a blind man.　H. 1 $\frac{1}{4}''$.

130. NETSUKE　　根付　人　物

By Miwa.　Edo Period.
Wood.　Design of a man.　H. 4 $\frac{1}{8}''$.

131. NETSUKE　　根付　恵比寿

By Chokusai.　Edo Period.
Ivory.　Design of Ebisu (god of good fortune).　H. 4 $\frac{1}{8}''$.

132. NETSUKE　　根付　達　磨

By Ryūchin.　Edo Period.
Ivory.　Design of Daruma.　H. $\frac{7}{8}''$.

　　　The Indian priest Daruma went to China where he established the Contemplative Sect of Buddhism. A legendary story tells that he sat in contemplation in a cave for nine years until he became lame.　He is frequently shown as a man with no limb at all.

133. NETSUKE　　根付　虎に猿

By Chokusai.　Edo Period.
Ivory.　Design of a tiger and a monkey.　H. 1 $\frac{1}{4}''$.

134. NETSUKE　根付　蛤

By Chokusai. Edo Period.
Ivory. Design of a clam shell. D. 1 $\frac{3}{4}$″.

135. NETSUKE　根付　犬

By Chokusai. Edo Period.
Ivory. Design of a dog. H. 1 $\frac{1}{4}$″.

136. NETSUKE　根付　鼠

By Chokusai. Edo Period.
Ivory. Design of a rat. D. 1 $\frac{1}{2}$″.

137. NETSUKE　根付　竜　宮

By Kagetoshi. Edo Period.
Ivory. Design of Ryūgū (a palace in the sea). H. 1 $\frac{1}{8}$″.

138. NETSUKE　根付　盧生の夢

By Kagetoshi. Edo Period.
Ivory. Design of Rosei. H. 1 $\frac{3}{8}$″.

　　Rosei (in Chinese: Lü Shêng) was an ambitious young student in the T'ang Dynasty. He one day dropped in at a wayside cottage and asked for a meal, soon falling asleep while waiting. In his dream he married a beautiful lady, became rich and rose to a prominent rank, and had a prosperous family with numerous children and grand-children. When he awoke, the meal had not yet been made ready. He learned that life was only ephemeral, and gave up his worldly ambition.

139. NETSUKE　根付　蓬萊　山

By Kagetoshi. Edo Period.
Ivory. Design of Hōrai. H. 1 $\frac{1}{2}$″.

　　Hōrai (in Chinese: Pêng-lai) is an island of Taoistic immortals in Chinese legends, said to be located in the "Eastern Ocean". It is said by some that Hōrai referred to Japan.

140. NETSUKE　根付　鶴

By Kagetoshi. Edo Period.
Ivory. Design of cranes. H. $\frac{7}{8}$″.

　　The crane symbolizes long life and nobility of character.

141—151　Pre-historic and proto-historic earthenwares

141. URN, JŌMON TYPE EARTHENWARE　　繩文式壺形土器

Jōmon Period.
H. 15 $\frac{1}{2}$″. D. of mouth 22 $\frac{7}{8}$″. From Tokyo-to.

　　This urn represents the style of Jōmon earthenware in the Kanto District (eastern part of Japan) in the middle of Jōmon Period.

142. BOWL, JŌMON TYPE EARTHENWARE 繩文式鉢形土器

Jōmon Period.
H. 7 ⅝″. W. 9 ½″. From Ibaragi-ken.

143. VESSEL ON TALL FOOT, JŌMON TYPE EARTHENWARE 繩文式高坏形土器

Jōmon Period.
H. 3 ⅜″. D. of mouth 7 ¼″. From Aomori-ken.

144. JAR, JŌMON TYPE EARTHENWARE 繩文式壺形土器

Jōmon Period.
H. 3 ¼″. D. of mouth 4 ⅛″. From Akita-ken.

Made of relatively fine, smooth clay and decorated with heavy raised ornaments, this piece illustrates a considerably advanced stage of the northeastern style of Jōmon ware.

145. EWER, JŌMON TYPE EARTHENWARE 繩文式注口土器

Jōmon Period.
H. 4 ¾″. W. 9 ¼″. Place of excavation unknown.

146. JAR, YAYOI TYPE EARTHENWARE 弥生式壺形土器

Yayoi Period.
H. 11 ⅞″. W. 10 ⅝″. From Mie-ken.

This is a fine example of Yayoi earthenware from the central part of Japan on the Pacific coast. The red paint gives it a beautiful effect.

147. STEM CUP, YAYOI TYPE EARTHENWARE 弥生式高坏形土器

Yayoi Period.
H. 6 ¾″. D. of mouth 9 ⅞″. From Aichi-ken.

148. POT ON TALL LEG WITH COVER, SUE TYPE EARTHENWARE 須恵器高脚付壺

Period of Ancient Burial Mounds.
H. 12 ¼″. W. 6 ⅞″. From Fukui-ken.

The Sue Type earthenware, made in a technique introduced from Silla and Paekche in Korea, was fashioned on the potter's wheel and high-fired in a pit kiln. Some of Sue pieces have a glaze, an accidental effect caused by wood-ashes falling on the surface during firing. The making of Sue ware was a hereditary craft.

149. STEM CUP WITH COVER, SUE TYPE EARTHENWARE 須恵器蓋付高坏

Period of Ancient Burial Mounds.
H. 10 ⅞″. W. 6 ¾″. From Okayama-ken.

150. VASE WITH TALL NECK, SUE TYPE EARTHENWARE 須恵器長頸壺

Period of Ancient Burial Mounds.
H. 9 ¼″. W. 6 ″. From Shizuoka-ken.

151. HORIZONTAL POT, SUE TYPE EARTHENWARE 須恵器横長瓶

Period of Ancient Burial Mounds.
H. 10 ¼″. L. 13 ¼″. From Gifu-ken.

152—174 *Pottery and porcelain of the historic periods*

152. JAR WITH FOUR EARS　須恵器四耳壺

Heian Period.
Wood-ash glazed.　H. 11 $\frac{7}{8}''$.

153. JAR WITH FOUR EARS　灰釉四耳刻模様壺

Kamakura Period.
Seto ware, wood-ash glaze.　With incised ornament.　H. 13 $\frac{3}{4}''$.　D. of mouth 4 $\frac{7}{8}''$.　D. of foot 5″.
From Shizuoka-ken.

154. JAR　飴釉印花模様壺

Kamakura Period.
Seto ware, dark-brown glaze.　With stamped ornament.　H. 9 $\frac{3}{4}''$.　D. of mouth 4 $\frac{3}{4}''$.　D. of foot 5 $\frac{5}{8}''$.

This jar was discovered under a stone monument which bore a date of 1327. Stamped ornaments, like the chrysanthemum patterns on this piece, began to be used frequently in the Kamakura Period. Probably they were copied from Chinese porcelain which was imported in quantity in this period.

155. JAR WITH FOUR EARS　褐釉四耳壺

Muromachi Period.
Seto ware, brown glaze.　Mark of Eishō era (1504—1520).　H. 13 $\frac{3}{4}''$. D. of mouth 5 $\frac{1}{8}''$. D. of foot 5 $\frac{1}{2}''$.

156. TEA CADDY　褐釉茶入

Muromachi Period.
Seto ware, brown glaze.　Shape of *suiteki* (ewer for writer's desk).　H. 2 $\frac{1}{2}''$.　D. of mouth 1 $\frac{3}{4}''$.　D. of foot 2 $\frac{1}{2}''$.

157. TEA CADDY　褐釉茶入

Muromachi Period.
Seto ware, brown glaze.　*Taikai* form (with large mouth and bulging body).　H. 2 $\frac{5}{8}''$.　D. of mouth 5 $\frac{5}{8}''$.　D. of foot 2 $\frac{1}{8}''$.

158. TEA-BOWL　黄瀬戸茶碗

Momoyama Period.
"Ki (Yellow) Seto" ware.　H. 3 $\frac{1}{4}''$.　D. of mouth 5 $\frac{5}{8}''$.　D. of foot 3 $\frac{5}{8}''$.

159. TEA-BOWL　志野筒茶碗

Momoyama Period.
Shino type (Seto group).　H. 4 $\frac{1}{2}''$.　D. of mouth 5″.　D. of foot 3″.

The type of pottery known as Shino was made in the eastern part of Gifu Prefecture. Shino pieces are mostly covered with a thick white feldspathic glaze, under which are painted simple graphic designs like this. Other varieties have no ornament, or have line-engraved designs on a mouse-gray body. The term is said to have been derived from a man named Shino in the Momoyama Period who possessed a vessel of this glaze color.

160. BOWL　　志野唐きび模様鉢

Momoyama Period.
Shino type (Seto group). Design of millets. H. 2 ½″. D. of mouth 11 ¼″. D. of foot 6 ½″.

161. TEA-BOWL　　織部黒茶碗

Momoyama Period.
"Oribe-guro (black)" type (Seto group). H. 3 ½″. D. of mouth 5 ¾″. D. of foot 2 ¾″.

The Oribe pottery was made in the same area and period as the Shino, but its glaze is thinner and its shapes are largely irregular. The name of this type is derived from Furuta Oribe-no-shō Shigenari, a distinguished tea master of the Keichō era (1596—1615), who favored this style of pottery.

162. INKSTONE　　青 織 部 硯

Momoyama Period.
"Ao (Green) Oribe" type (Seto group). L. 6 ¾″. W. 6 ⅛″. H. 1 ⅛″.

163. PITCHER　　色絵牡丹模様水指　　仁清作

By Ninsei. Edo Period.
Kyoto ware, over-glaze colors. Design of peonies. H. 5 ⅜″. D. of mouth 3 ⅞″. D. of foot 4″.

Ninsei was a great genius who established the graceful style of Kyoto pottery around the middle of the seventeenth century. He was skilled especially in decorating pottery pieces in over-glaze enamels as well as gold and silver, with which he beautifully reproduced the elegant effect of *maki-e* lacquer.

164. SQUARE DISH　　黒絵観鷗図角皿　　光琳絵乾山作

By Kenzan. Edo Period.
Kyoto ware, iron-black painting over glaze. Design of a poet viewing wild-geese in flight. H. 1 ⅛″. 8 ¾″ square.

Next to Ninsei in fame in Kyoto ware was Kenzan, who had his factory at Narutaki in the north-western outskirt of Kyoto city. He and his elder brother, Kōrin, made numbers of joint works, Kōrin doing the painting, as on this present piece. The design shows the Chinese poet Kō Sankoku (Huang Shan-ku) of the Sung Dynasty who enjoyed the sight of wild-geese in flight.

165. TIER OF LUNCHEON BOXES　　色 絵 重 箱　　京 焼

Edo Period.
"Ko (Old) Kiyomizu" type (Kyoto ware), over-glaze enamels. H. 9 ⅞″

166. BOWL　　銹絵雪笹模様鉢　　仁阿弥道八作

By Nin-ami Dōhachi. Edo Period.
Kyoto ware, iron-black painting over glaze. Design of snow on bamboo leaves. H. 5″. D. of mouth 11 ¼″. D. of foot 5 ½″.

The design of bush-bamboo in snow is one of the favorite subjects of ornamentation on the ceramic wares of Kyoto. Dōhachi was a representative of Kyoto pottery in the late Edo Period, specializing in the graceful, pure Japanese style traditional since the time of Ninsei.

167. DISH　色絵兜花模様皿　　古九谷

Edo Period.
Kutani ware, over-glaze enamels.　Design of *kabuto-bana* flowers.　H. 2 ⅝″.　D. 12 ¼″.　D. of foot 6 ⅛″.

　　　　Kutani ware from Kaga (now Ishikawa Prefecture) is one of the representative types of Japanese enamelled porcelain.　The Kutani factory was active for only a short period from the middle to the late seventeenth century, after which it was abandoned until the "restored Kutani" ware began to be produced in the early nineteenth century.　The Kutani ware from this first period is called "Old Kutani".

168. DISH　色絵竹虎模様皿　　柿右衛門

Edo Period.
Kakiemon style, over-glaze enamels.　Design of tiger and bamboos.　H. 2 ½″.　D. 8″.　D. of foot 5 ⅜″.

　　　　This is a typical Kakiemon porcelain with the ornament painted in polished brushwork in red, green and yellow overglazes on the characteristic milk-white surface.　Kakiemon I in the mid-seventeenth century is famous as the originator of fine white porcelain, and subsequently enamelled porcelain, in Japan. The name Kakiemon has been inherited in the family through generations, the present Kakiemon being the twelfth.　This dish dates from the middle of the Edo Period, namely around the time of Kakiemon VI.

169. BOWL　色絵琴高仙人図鉢　　伊万里

Edo Period.
Imari ware, over-glaze enamels.　Design of Kinkō Sennin (a Taoistic immortal).　H. 3 ⅜″.　D. 9″.　D. of foot 4 ½″.

　　　　After Kakiemon succeeded in producing the first enamelled porcelain in Japan, the Arita area in Saga (Kyushu) became famous for porcelain manufacture.　Because products of this area were shipped from the neighboring port of Imari, they were known as Imari ware.

170. DISH　色絵柴垣模様皿　　鍋島焼

Edo Period.
Nabeshima ware, over-glaze enamels.　Design of brushwood fence.　H. 2 ½″. D. 12″.　D. of foot 6 ½″.

　　　　Nabeshima is a type of porcelain made at the official ceramic factory maintained by the Nabeshima Family ruling what is now Saga Prefecture in Kyushu during the feudal period.　Characterized by its precise forms and elaborate, dignified ornaments, it is known as the finest of Japanese enamelled porcelain. Nabeshima pieses, reserved for official use by the lords there, were not available in the public market, and therefore were especially valued as rarities.

171. DISH　色絵籠目模様皿　　鍋島焼

Edo Period.
Nabeshima ware, over-glaze enamels. Design of basketwork.　H. 2 ⅜″. D. 8 ⅞″. D. of foot 4 ⅜″.

172. DISH　色絵桜模様皿　　鍋島焼

Edo Period.
Nabeshima ware, over-glaze enamels.　Design of cherry blossoms.　Measurements same as 171.

173. DISH   褐釉飛白模様皿   小代焼

Edo Period.

Shōdai ware, brown glaze with white spots. H. 1 ⅜″. D. 11 ¾″.

The Shōdai factory in Kumamoto Prefecture (Kyushu) was founded in 1632, and was abandoned in the late nineteenth century. Its products are a ware of ferruginous clay covered with opaque "muddy" glazes.

174. TEA-BOWL   赤 楽 茶 碗   玉水弥兵衛作

By Tamamizu Yahei. Edo Period.

Kyoto ware, "Aka (Red) Raku" type. H. 3 ½″.

Yahei, active in the middle of the seventeenth century, was skilled in copying the style of Kōetsu, the famous handicraft genius in the beginning of the same century. The Kōetsu style is well reproduced in this tea-bowl with a gently curving basal portion and a small, low foot.

175-209 Fabrics

175—181. SAMPLES OF ANCIENT FABRICS

Nara Period.

16 ⅛″ × 11 ⅝″ each.

175. Weft-weave brocade (compound twill). Floral design on green ground.   碧地花模様錦裂
176. Weft-weave brocade (compound twill). Floral design on red ground.   赤地花模様錦裂
177. *Kyōkechi* ("jammed dyeing"). Quatrefoil patterns on silk.   四稜模様絁地纐纈裂
178. *Kyōkechi*. Floral design on silk gauze.   花模様羅地纐纈裂
179. *Kōkechi* (tie-dyeing). Red hemp.   赤麻地纐纈裂
180. *Rōkechi* (batik). Design of flowers-and-birds on purple-red silk.   蘇芳絁地花鳥模様﨟纈裂
181. Sock. Hand-painted design on hemp.   麻 地 描 絵 襪

The Shōsō-in Repository of Imperial Treasures, located in the precinct of the Tōdai-ji Monastery in Nara, contains textiles and costume ornaments used at the consecration ceremony of the Great Buddha in the monastery in 752. These seven fragmentary pieces from the collection illustrate the weaving and dyeing techniques of the eighth century. They include compound twill and gauze weaves, as well as dyeworks in tie-dyeing, wax-resist dyeing (batik), and "jammed dyeing". In this last-mentioned method, the cloth is folded up, jammed between two boards with perforated design, and dyed, the design on one half of the cloth being a mirror-reflection of the other.

182. NŌ ROBE OF ATSU-ITA KARA-ORI TYPE   浅黄地鉄線花模様厚板唐織能衣裳

Edo Period.

Light-blue silk in brocaded weave. Design of clematis. H. 60 ⅛″.

This type is worn by the hero of a *Nō* drama.

183. NŌ ROBE OF KARA-ORI TYPE   赤段青海波籬に秋草模様唐織能衣裳

Edo Period.

Red silk in brocaded weave. Design of bands of *sei-gai-ha* (conventionalized wave patterns), and autumn grasses along hedges. H. 57 ⅜″.

Used for the role of a lady or a young nobleman.

184. NŌ ROBE OF NUI-HAKU TYPE   紫綸子地団扇模様縫箔能衣裳

Edo Period.
Purple figured silk, with embroidery and gold-leaf imprint.   Design of round fans. H. 57 ⅜″.

The *nui-haku* ("embroidery and gold-leaf imprint") is used mostly as a *koshi-maki* (summer outer garment worn over the kimono, tied over with a sash and with the upper half turned down at the sash) for a female role in *Nō* dramas.

185. NŌ ROBE OF NUI-HAKU TYPE   白綸子地木賊鎌模様縫箔能衣裳

Edo Period.
White figured silk, with embroidery and gold-leaf imprint. Design of sickles and *tokusa* (scouring rush). H. 65 ⅝″.

186. KOSODE   白綸子地紅葉に笠模様小袖

Edo Period.
White figured silk.   Design of maples and hats.   H. 58 ½″.

The *kosode* ("short hanging-sleeves") was originally an under garment used by men and ladies of upper classes, who used to wear many layers of clothing. Later on, it began to be worn as the top garment, and was decorated with beautiful colorful designs.   The present-day form of kimono developed from the *kosode*.

187. KOSODE   白繻地桜花に扇面模様小袖

Edo Period.
White satin-weave silk, with embroidery.   Design of cherry blossoms and fans.   H. 63 ⅝″.

188. KOSODE   赤縮緬地菊に芙蓉模様小袖

Edo Period.
Red silk crepe.   Design of chrysanthemum and hibiscus flowers. H. 60 ⅞″.

189. KOSODE   浅黄地流水に花丸模様小袖

Edo Period.
Light-blue silk. Design of water-streams and rounded flowers. H. 63 ⅛″.

190. FURISODE   白綸子地簾に橘模様振袖

Edo Period.
White figured silk.   Design of rush curtains and mandarin-orange trees.   H. 64 ⅞″.

The *furisode* ("swinging hanging-sleeves") is a kimono with long hanging-sleeves detached from the body, as discriminated from the *tome-sode* ("fixed sleeves") which has the hanging-sleeves sewn to the sides.   It is chiefly used by young girls.

191. FURISODE   赤綸子地鶴模様総絞振袖

Edo Period.
Red figured silk, with tie-dyeing. Design of cranes. H. 60 ⅞″.

192. UCHIKAKE 赤綸子地君ケ代模様打掛

Edo Period.
Red figured silk. Design of a poem entitled *Kimi ga yo*. H. 64 ⅜″.

The *uchikake* is a lady's ceremonial gown worn over the kimono.

193. UCHIKAKE 緑縮緬地風景模様打掛

Edo Period.
Green silk crepe. Design of a landscape. H. 66 ¾″.

194. KATABIRA 浅黄麻地山水に和歌模様帷子

Edo Period.
Light-blue hemp. Design of landscapes and poems. H. 64 ½″.

Hemp kimono termed *katabira*, usually in elaborate blue dyework with resist of rice paste, was the most expensive type of summer clothing.

195. KATABIRA 薄黄麻地蔦に飛鳥模様帷子

Edo Period.
Light yellow hemp. Design of ivy and birds in flight. H. 60″.

196. SASH 紫繻子地石畳菊模様掛下帯

Edo Period.
Purple satin-weave silk. Design of checkers and chrysanthemums. L. 172 ½″.

This and the following sashes are *kakeshita-obi*, used over the kimono under an *uchikake*.

197. SASH 緑繻子地牡丹模様掛下帯

Edo Period.
Green satin-weave silk. Design of peonies. L. 167″

198. FIRE COAT 武家火事装束

Edo Period.
Wool. H. 38 ¾″.

Gentlemen and ladies of the samurai class wore such coats at the time of a fire. These coats, like the present specimen made of wool, were sometimes more ornamental than practical. Wool was a luxurious imported stuff at the time.

199. FIRE COAT 町方火事装束

Edo Period.
Cotton. H. 37″.

This specimen was made for use by firemen of the commoners' class.

200—209. SAMPLES OF CLOTHING FABRICS　衣　裳　裂

Edo Period.

23 $\frac{5}{8}$″ × 12 $\frac{3}{8}$″ each.

200. Brown plain-weave silk, with embroidery and gold-leaf imprint.　Design of wistaria and pines.
茶平絹地藤松模様縫箔裂

201. Brown plain-weave silk, with embroidery and gold-leaf imprint. Design of fans and *tanzaku* (oblong sheets of paper for painting or poem writing)
茶地扇面短冊模様縫箔裂

202. Black figured silk.　Design of flowering plants.
黒綸子地花卉模様裂

203. Red figured silk.　Design of flowering plants.
赤綸子地花卉模様裂

204. Black figured silk.　Design of flowers-and-birds.
黒綸子地花鳥模様裂

205. Black plain-weave silk, with embroidery.　Design of pines, bamboos, prunus-trees and cranes.
黒平絹地松竹梅鶴模様刺繍裂

206. Black figured silk.　Design of fans and clematis.
黒綸子地扇面鉄線花模様裂

207. Purple figured silk.　Design of waterfalls and flowers.
紫綸子地滝に花模様裂

208. Light blue silk crepe.　Design of noblemen's boats.
浅黄縮緬地御座船模様裂

209. White and brown hemp. Design of peonies and screens.
白麻地牡丹障子模様裂

PERIODS OF JAPANESE ART HISTORY

Pre-historic periods

    Jōmon Period   — B. C. 3rd – 2nd c.

    Yayoi Period   B. C. 3rd – 2nd c. — A. D. 2nd – 3rd c.

Proto-historic period

    Period of Ancient Burial Mounds   A. D. 3rd c. — 551

Historic periods

Asuka Period	552— 645
Nara Period	646— 793
Early Nara Period	646— 709
Late Nara Period	710— 793
Heian Period	794—1184
Early Heian Period	794— 896
Late Heian Period	897—1184
Kamakura Period	1185—1333
Muromachi Period	1334—1567
Momoyama Period	1568—1614
Edo Period	1615—1867

Abbreviations

H.	height	L.	length
W.	width	D.	diameter
C.	century		

PLATES

5 *HANIWA* FIGURE OF DOG 埴輪犬
Period of Ancient Burial Mounds

1 CLAY FIGURINE 土偶
Jōmon Period

2 CLAY FIGURINE
Jōmon Period 土偶

3 *HANIWA* FIGURE OF MAN 埴輪男子
Period of Ancient Burial Mounds

6 *HANIWA* MODEL OF HOUSE 埴輪家
Period of Ancient Burial Mounds

4 *HANIWA* FIGURE OF WOMAN
Period of Ancient Burial Mounds
埴輪女子

7 MIROKU BOSATSU
Nara Period
彌勒菩薩半跏像

8 MIROKU BOSATSU
Nara Period
彌勒菩薩半跏像

9 JUICHIMEN KANNON
Nara Period
十一面觀音立像

12 DAINICHI NYORAI 大日如來坐像
Heian Period

11 PRIEST JION DAISHI 慈恩大師坐像
Heian Period

48

10 TAISHAKU TEN
Heian Period
帝釋天立像

13 AMIDA NYORAI
Kamakura Period
阿彌陀如來立像

14 MEKIRA TAISHŌ
Kamakura Period
迷企羅大將立像

15 MINAMOTO YORITOMO 源賴朝坐像
Kamakura Period

16 GIGAKU MASK "RIKISHI"
Nara Period 伎樂面 力士

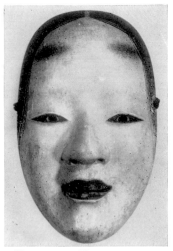

17 NŌ MASK, "ŌMI ONNA"
Muromachi Period 能面 近江女

18 NŌ MASK, "WARAI JŌ"
Muromachi Period 能面 笑尉

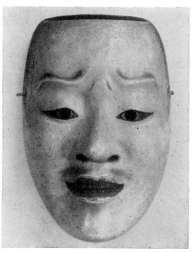

19 NŌ MASK, "WAKA OTOKO"
Momoyama Period 能面 若男

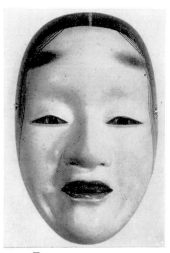

20 NŌ MASK, "FUKAI"
Edo Period 能面 深井

21 NŌ MASK, "DŌJI"
Edo Period　能面　童子

22 NŌ MASK, "SHIKAMI"
Edo Period　能面　顰見

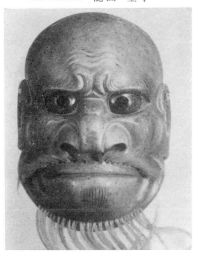

23 NŌ MASK, "BESHIMI AKUJŌ"
Edo Period　能面　癋見悪尉

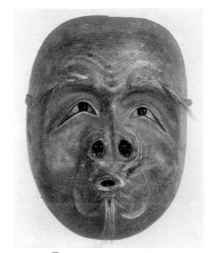

24 KYŌGEN MASK, "USOBUKI"
Muromachi Period 狂言面 ウソブキ

25 KYŌGEN MASK, "BUAKU"
Momoyama Period　狂言面　武悪

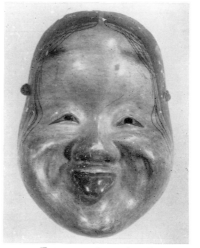

26 KYŌGEN MASK, "SHITAKIRI-
HIME" Edo Period　狂言面　舌切姫

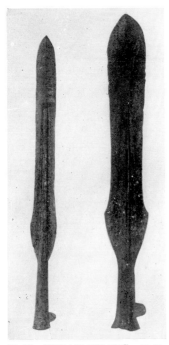

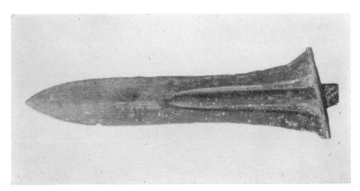

27, 28 SPEAR HEADS 銅鉾
Yayoi Period

29 HALBERD 銅戈
Yayoi Period

30 _DŌTAKU_ 銅鐸
Yayoi Period

31 _DŌTAKU_ 銅鐸
Yayoi Period

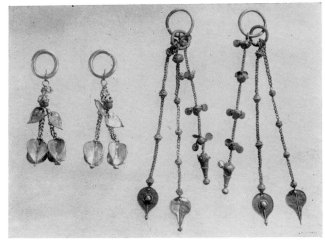

36, 37 EAR-RINGS Period of Ancient Burial Mounds 金製耳飾

32 BRACELET WITH BELLS 銅鈴釧
Period of Ancient Burial Mounds

38~42 *MAGA-TAMA* Period of Ancient Burial Mounds 勾玉

33, 34 BRACELETS Period of Ancient Burial Mounds 石釧

35 BRACELET IN SHAPE OF A SPADE BLADE 鍬形石
Period of Ancient Burial Mounds

43 CINERARY URN Nara Period 金銅壺

44 **BUDDHIST RITUAL VASE**
Nara Period 銅水瓶

45 **HEAD OF A** *SHAKUJŌ*
Nara Period 錫杖頭

47 *KEI* Heian Period 蓮池模様磬

46 **BUDDHIST RITUAL BELL**
Heian Period 八佛浮彫五鈷鈴

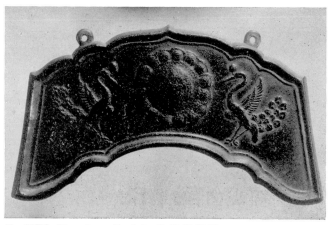

48 *KEI* Kamakura Period 孔雀模様磬

51 **DRAGON HEAD** 龍 頭
Muromachi Period

50 **HANGING LANTERN** 梅竹透模樣釣燈籠
Muromachi Period

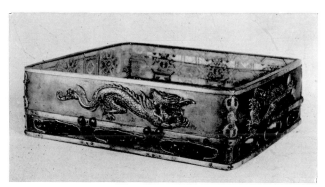

49 *SUE-BAKO* 龍模樣居箱
Kamakura Period

52 **TEA-CEREMONY KETTLE** 茶 釜
Muromachi Period

53 **TEA-CEREMONY KETTLE** 茶 釜
Momoyama Period

55 **MIRROR** 鼉龍模樣鏡
Period of Ancient Burial Mounds

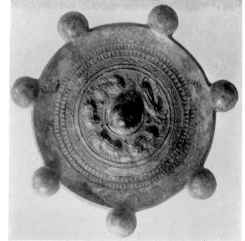

56 **MIRROR WITH BELLS** 七鈴鏡
Period of Ancient Burial Mounds

57 **EIGHT-FOLIATE MIRROR**
Heian Period 瑞花鳳凰模樣八稜鏡

58 **MIRROR** 秋草蝶鳥模樣鏡
Heian Period

54 MIRROR 二神二獸模樣鏡
Period of Ancient Burial Mounds

59 MIRROR 松枝双鶴模樣鏡
Heian Period

60 EIGHT-FOLIATE MIRROR
Heian Period 瑞花模樣八稜鏡

61 FIVE-LOBED MIRROR
Kamakura Period 瑞花模樣五花鏡

63 MIRROR 菊花蝶鳥模樣鏡
Kamakura Period

62 MIRROR 甜瓜蝶鳥模樣鏡
Kamakura Period

64 **MIRROR** 橘樹双鶴模様鏡
Muromachi Period

65 **CHAMFERED SQUARE MIRROR**
Momoyama Period 菊桐模様角切方鏡

66 **MIRROR WITH HANDLE**
Edo Period 菊花模様柄鏡

67 **MIRROR WITH HANDLE**
Edo Period 葡萄棚模様柄鏡

58

68 ARMOR OF *GUSOKU* TYPE　二枚胴具足
Momoyama Period

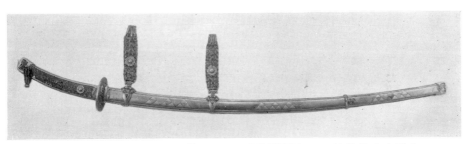

69 SWORD MOUNTING OF *HYŌGO-GUSARI* TYPE　三鱗模様兵庫鎖太刀
Kamakura Period

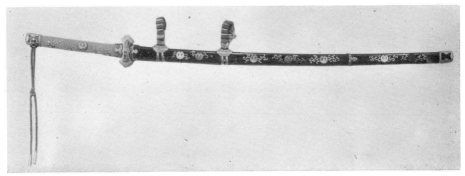

70 SWORD MOUNTING OF *KAZA-TACHI* TYPE　赤木螺鈿飾太刀
Muromachi Period

71 SWORD MOUNTING OF *KOSHI-GATANA* TYPE　牡丹浮模樣腰刀
Muromachi Period

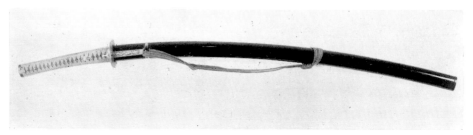

72 SWORD MOUNTING OF *UCHI-GATANA* TYPE　黑漆薰革打刀拵
Momoyama Period

73 SWORD MOUNTING OF *ITOMAKI-NO-TACHI* TYPE　糸卷太刀拵
Edo Period

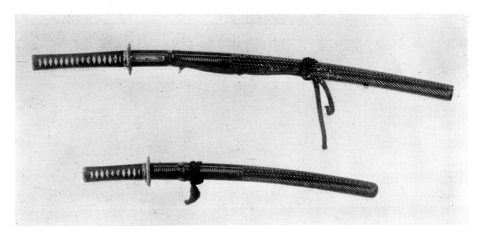

74 SWORD MOUNTING FOR *DAI-SHO*　黑蠟色刻鞘大小拵
Edo Period

75 GUARD 蟹透模様鐔
Muromachi Period

76 GUARD 二ツ巴透模様鐔
Muromachi Period

77 GUARD 野晒圖鐔
Muromachi Period

78 GUARD 八ツ蕨手透模様鐔
Momoyama Period

79 GUARD 猛禽捕猿圖鐔
Momoyama Period

80 GUARD 文字鐔
Edo Period

81 GUARD 木賊刈圖鐔
Edo Period

82 GUARD 雪花模様散七寶圖鐔
Edo Period

84 GUARD 鯉圖鐔
Edo Period

61

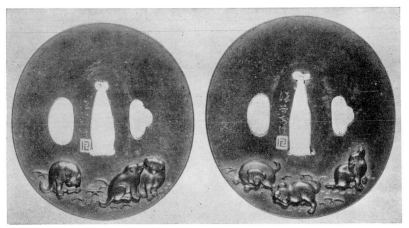

83 GUARDS FOR *DAI-SHO* 狗兒圖大小鐔
Edo Period

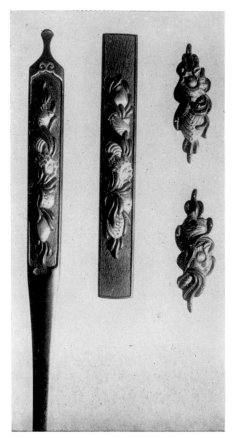

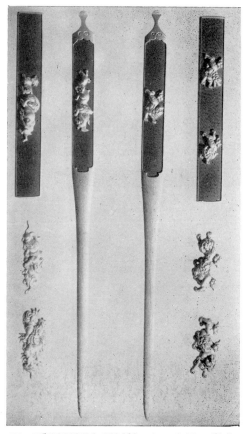

85 *MITOKORO-MONO* 藻草に貝模様三所物
Muromachi Period

87 *MITOKORO-MONO* 十二支圖三所物
Edo Period

86 *MITOKORO-MONO* 獅子圖三所物
Momoyama Period

88 SADDLE 萩模様螺鈿鞍
Heian Period

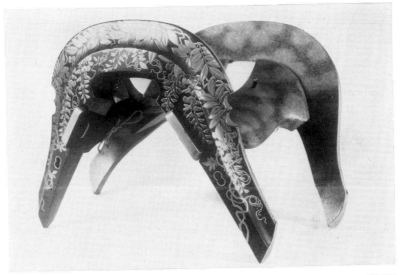

89 SADDLE AND STIRRUPS 藤模様蒔絵鞍及鐙
Edo Period

90 *GYŌYŌ* 杏葉
Period of Ancient Burial Mounds

91 *GYOYO* 杏葉
Period of Ancient Burial Mounds

92, 93 *HORSE BELLS* 馬鐸
Period of Ancient Burial Mounds

94 *HORSE BELL* 馬鈴
Period of Ancient Burial
Mounds

95 STIRRUPS   壺鐙
Period of Ancient Burial Mounds

96 *TEBAKO* 千鳥模樣蒔繪手箱
Kamakura Period

98 TEBAKO 扇面散模樣蒔繪手箱
Muromachi Period

97 INCENSE CONTAINER 花鳥模樣蒔繪香合
Kamakura Period

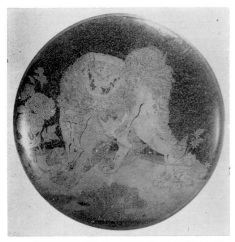

99 MIRROR BOX 獅子模樣蒔繪鏡箱
Muromachi Period

100 INCENSE CABINET 秋草模樣蒔繪香簞笥
Momoyama Period

101 SUTRA BOX 蓮池模様蒔絵崩經箱
Momoyama Period

102 DESK AND INKSTONE-BOX 蔦の細道,角田川模様蒔絵文臺及硯箱
Edo Period

104 MIRROR RACK 竹菱葵模樣蒔繪鏡臺
Edo Period

103 TOOTH-STAIN SET
Edo Period
竹菱葵模樣蒔繪齒黑箱

105 TRAYS 人物圖漆繪膳
Edo Period

106   107   108

106—110 *INRŌ* 印籠
Edo Period

109   110

111 *INRŌ* 印 籠
Edo Period

112   113   114

115   116   117   118

119   120   121   122

123 124 125 126

127 128 129 130

131 132 133 134 135

136 137 138 139 140

**143 VESSEL ON TALL FOOT,
JŌMON TYPE EARTHENWARE**
Jōmon Period 繩文式高坏形土器

**141 URN, JŌMON TYPE
EARTHENWARE**
Jōmon Period 繩文式壺形土器

144 JAR, JŌMON TYPE EARTHENWARE
Jōmon Period 繩文式壺形土器

**142 BOWL, JŌMON TYPE
EARTHENWARE**
Jōmon Period 繩文式鉢形土器

145 EWER, JŌMON TYPE EARTHENWARE
Jōmon Period 繩文式注口土器

143   JAR, YAYOI TYPE EARTHENWARE
Yayoi Period   彌生式壺形土器

**147   STEM CUP, YAYOI TYPE
EARTHENWARE**
Yayoi Period   彌生式高坏形土器

**148   POT ON TALL LEG WITH
COVER, SUE TYPE
EARTHENWARE**
Period of Ancient Burial Mounds
須惠器高脚付壺

**149   STEM CUP WITH COVER,
SUE TYPE EARTHENWARE**
Period of Ancient Burial Mounds
須惠器蓋付高坏

**150 VASE WITH TALL NECK, SUE
TYPE EARTHENWARE** 須惠器長頸壺
Period of Ancient Burial Mounds

**151 HORIZONTAL POT, SUE TYPE
EARTHENWARE** 須惠器橫長瓶
Period of Ancient Burial Mounds

153 SETO JAR WITH FOUR EARS
Kamakura Period 灰釉四耳刻模樣壺

152 JAR WITH FOUR EARS 須惠器四耳壺
Heian Period

154 SETO JAR 飴釉印花模樣壺
Kamakura Period

156 SETO TEA CADDY 褐釉茶入
Muromachi Period

155 SETO JAR WITH FOUR EARS
Muromachi Period 褐釉四耳壺

157 SETO TEA CADDY 褐釉茶入
Muromachi Period

158 "YELLOW SETO" TEA-BOWL 黄瀬戸茶碗
Momoyama Period

159 SHINO TEA-BOWL 志野筒茶碗
Momoyama Period

163 PITCHER by Ninsei　色繪牡丹模樣水指
Edo Period

160 SHINO BOWL 志野唐きび模様鉢
Momoyama Period

164 SQUARE DISH by Kenzan
Edo Period 黑繪觀鷗圖角皿

161 "BLACK ORIBE" TEA BOWL 織部黒茶碗
Momoyama Period

162 "GREEN ORIBE" INKSTONE 青織部硯
Momoyama Period

165 "OLD KIYOMIZU" TIER OF LUNCHEON BOXES 色繪重箱
Edo Period

167 KUTANI DISH 色繪兜花模樣皿
Edo Period

166 BOWL by Dōhachi
Edo Period 銹繪雪笹模樣鉢

168 KAKIEMON DISH 色繪竹虎模樣皿
Edo Period

169 IMARI BOWL 色繪琴高仙模樣鉢
Edo Period

170 NABESHIMA DISH 色繪柴垣模様皿
Edo Period

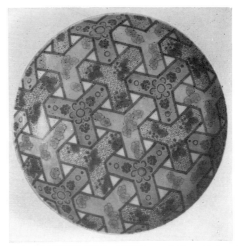

171 NABESHIMA DISH 色繪籠目模様皿
Edo Period

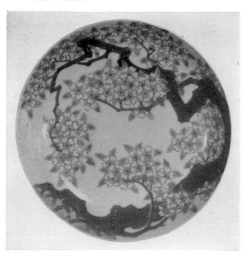

172 NABESHIMA DISH 色繪櫻模様皿
Edo Period

173 SHŌDAI DISH 褐釉飛白模様皿
Edo Period

174 "RED RAKU" TEA-BOWL 赤樂茶碗
Edo Period

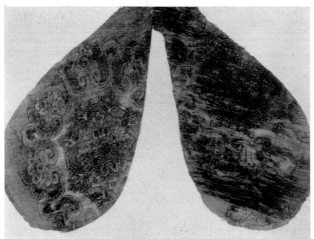

176 WEFT-WEAVE BROCADE 赤地花模様錦裂

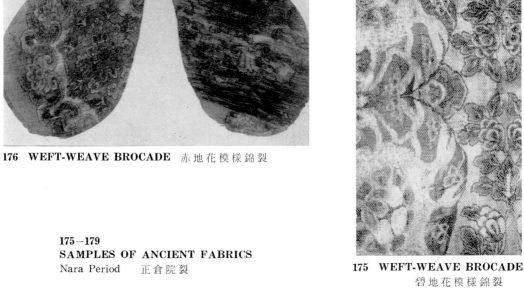

175—179
SAMPLES OF ANCIENT FABRICS
Nara Period　正倉院裂

175 WEFT-WEAVE BROCADE
碧地花模様錦裂

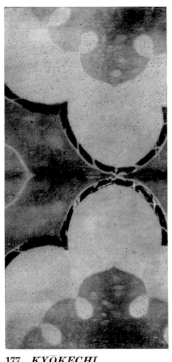

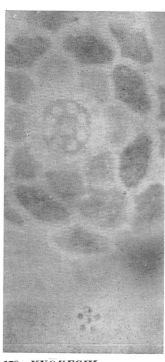

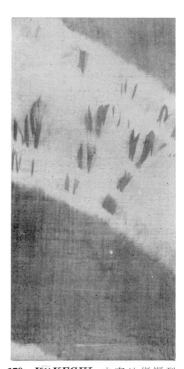

177 *KYOKECHI*
四稜模様絁地纐纈裂

178 *KYOKECHI*
花模様羅地纐纈裂

179 *KOKECHI* 赤㡧地纈纈裂

82

182 NŌ ROBE OF ATSU-ITA KARA-ORI TYPE
Edo Period 淺黃地鐵線花模樣厚板唐織能衣裳

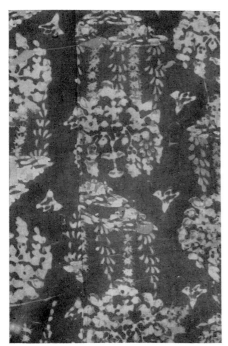

180 *ROKECHI* 蘇芳絁地花鳥模様﨟纈裂

181 SOCK 瓻地描繪襪

180—181
SAMPLES OF ANCIENT FABRICS
Nara Period 正倉院裂

183 *NŌ* ROBE OF KARA-ORI TYPE
Edo Period 赤段青海波﨟に秋草模様唐織能衣裳

184 *NŌ* ROBE OF NUI-HAKU TYPE
Edo Period 紫綸子地團扇模様縫箔能衣裳

185 *NO* **ROBE OF NUI-HAKU TYPE**
Edo Period　白綸子地木賊鎌模樣縫箔能衣裳

186　*KOSODE*　白綸子地紅葉に笠模樣小袖
Edo Period

187　*KOSODE*　白綸地櫻花に扇面模樣小袖
Edo Period

188 *KOSODE*　赤縮緬地菊に芙蓉模様小袖
Edo Period

189 *KOSODE*　淺黄地流水に花丸模様小袖
Edo Period

190 *FURISODE*　白綸子地簾橘模様振袖
Edo Period

191 *FURISODE* 赤綸子地鶴模様總絞振袖
Edo Period

192 *UCHIKAKE* 赤綸子地君ヶ代模様打掛
Edo Period

193 *UCHIKAKE* 綠縮緬地風景模様打掛
Edo Period

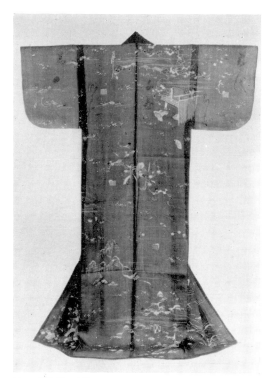

194 *KATABIRA* 淺黃麻地山水に和歌模樣帷子
Edo Period

195 *KATABIRA* 薄黃麻地蔦に飛鳥模樣帷子
Edo Period

196 SASH Edo Period
紫繻子地石疊菊模樣掛下帶

197 SASH Edo Period
綠繻子地牡丹模樣掛下帶

89

198 FIRE COAT 武家火事装束
Edo Period

199 FIRE COAT 町方火事装束
Edo Period

200

**SAMPLES
OF CLOTHING
FABRICS** 衣裳裂
Edo Period

201   202

203   204   205

206—209

SAMPLES OF

CLOTHING

FABRICS 衣裳裂

Edo Period

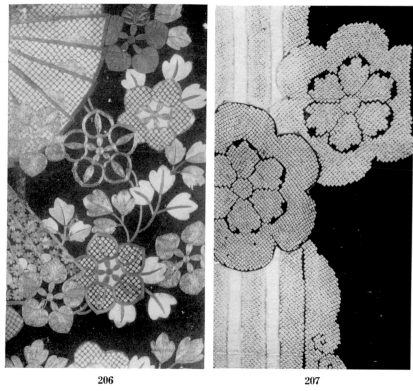

206

207

208

209